HIGH-FREQUENCY
AMPLIFIERS

HIGH-FREQUENCY AMPLIFIERS

Ralph S. Carson
University of Missouri • Rolla

A WILEY-INTERSCIENCE PUBLICATION

JOHN WILEY & SONS

New York / London / Sydney / Toronto

Library of Congress Cataloging in Publication Data:

Carson, Ralph S
  High-frequency amplifiers.

  "A Wiley-Interscience publication."
  Bibliography: p.
  Includes index.
    1. Transistor amplifiers.   I.   Title.

TK7871.2.C35   621.38′0282   75-8780
ISBN 0–471–13705–7

Printed in the United States of America

10 9 8 7 6 5 4 3 2

PREFACE

This book presents principles and techniques useful in the analysis and design of high-frequency amplifiers. It is intended primarily as a textbook for a single-semester course for beginning graduate and senior undergraduate students in electrical engineering, but it can also be used by practicing engineers as a source of information about high-frequency amplifiers. It emphasizes the use of the Smith chart and scattering parameters, both of which are fundamental to this area of analysis and design.

This textbook is unusual compared to other books on electronic circuits because it develops the Smith chart into a useful design aid. The Smith chart is part of the graphical heritage in electrical engineering, but students have had little opportunity to discover the potential and insight that it offers in electronic circuit applications. Preparing this material on applications of the Smith chart has been one of the most exciting and rewarding aspects of writing the book. The material has been collected from many sources scattered throughout the literature; it has been integrated and explained with numerous examples.

Chapter 1 reviews two-port transistor parameters and their conversion relationships. The indefinite admittance matrix is discussed to take advantage of its usefulness for calculating parameters when changing transistor configuration between common base, common emitter, and common collector. The calculus of deviations is introduced only as an additional method for calculating parameters when changing configuration. Criteria for activity and passivity are derived in terms of admittance parameters; then the maximum frequency of oscillation is determined for the high-frequency hybrid-π model of the transistor.

Chapter 2 reviews the impedance and gain properties of a linear active transistor with terminations at its two ports and expresses input and output

v

immittances in terms of generalized parameters. Stability and instability are discussed and conditions for inherent stability derived and also expressed in terms of generalized parameters. Unilateral power gain, tunability, and bandwidths are discussed.

Chapter 3 introduces the Smith chart and develops its use in designing various types of immittance matching networks. How to find transmission line input and output impedances, reciprocals of immittances, and how to locate negative resistances are described. The design of lumped-constant matching networks, microstrip and some of its properties, and the design of microstrip matching networks are described in detail.

Chapter 4 is devoted to unilateral amplifiers, and the cascode circuit is discussed. Some history of the origins of Q puts that important quantity in perspective. Mathematical series-parallel transformations are applied to the design of matching networks to supplement the Smith chart. Obtaining optimum terminations for a specified bandwidth is discussed. The chapter also explains how power, voltage, and current gains can be shown on the Smith chart as families of circles. A major advantage of using the Smith chart in such cases is that the gains expected for all possible passive terminations are displayed completely.

Chapter 5 deals with nonunilateral amplifiers. Power-gain circles are drawn on the Smith chart and used with a given tunability factor to determine the output termination. It is shown how a rectangular grid can be drawn on the Smith chart to determine input admittance of a transistor for any passive output termination. Design procedures for potentially unstable transistors are discussed. A new mismatching technique is presented in detail. Circuit instability caused by the emitter circuit is described.

Chapter 6 introduces scattering parameters, their conversion relationships with other parameters, their physical meanings, and methods for calculating and measuring them. Criteria for activity and passivity, potential instability, the indefinite scattering matrix, and directional couplers are discussed.

Chapter 7 is devoted to amplifier design using scattering parameters. It is shown how generalized scattering parameters for arbitrary terminations are calculated and used in the design of unilateral and nonunilateral amplifiers. Power-gain circles are again drawn on the Smith chart, and stable and unstable regions identified. The conditions for inherent stability and for simultaneous conjugate matching are derived and used. The chapter ends with a design procedure for use with potentially unstable transistors.

Appendixes A and B provide further details of derivations that are not found anywhere else in the literature. General references consisting of the original papers and alternative procedures are given in the bibliography.

Many other important aspects of high-frequency amplifiers had to be omitted from a book of this size. Topics such as noise, neutralization, biasing, multistage circuits, and computer-aided design are adequately covered elsewhere.

It is assumed the reader has a general knowledge of circuit theory, transistor circuits, and of basic matrix manipulations. Some background in transmission lines at high frequencies is helpful but not essential. The book contains a large number of worked examples to illustrate techniques and provides problems at the end of each chapter. All of the material, except for last-minute revisions, has been used with gratifying results in various graduate and senior courses at University of Missouri–Rolla and at the Graduate Engineering Center of UMR in St. Louis.

I thank the many students who have suggested improvements in earlier versions of these chapters. In particular, I thank David Mundis, Russell Woirhaye, and Frank Giannoti for investigating some of the design details in their senior seminar papers. Most of all, I thank Dr. K. Kurokawa for giving me insight into some of the more elusive properties of scattering parameters.

RALPH S. CARSON

Rolla, Missouri
February 1975

CONTENTS

HIGH-FREQUENCY
AMPLIFIERS

CHAPTER ONE

TRANSISTOR PARAMETERS

1-0 INTRODUCTION

Transistors are three-terminal devices. In use, one of the terminals is common to both the input and output circuits. This leads to the familiar configurations known as common base (CB), common emitter (CE), and common collector (CC). The common terminal also is often connected to the reference ground.

The common terminal can be paired with one or the other of the two remaining terminals. Each pair is called a port, and two pairs are possible for any of the basic CB, CE, CC configurations. Such circuits are properly called two-port networks. The two ports are usually identified as an input port and as an output port. The collector is not used with an input terminal except in certain special applications. The usual connections are summarized in Fig. 1-1.

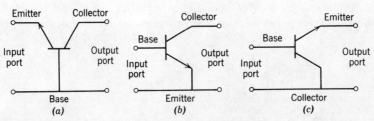

Figure 1-1. *Basic transistor configurations: (a) common base; (b) common emitter; (c) common collector.*

1

1-1 TWO-PORT TRANSISTOR PARAMETERS

Basically, electronic circuits are used to process information. Originally, the information may be nonelectrical in nature such as heat, sound, pressure, or humidity. In such cases, a transducer is required to convert the information into its electrical equivalent before the transistor can do its job. The electrical information is called a signal, and it exists in the forms of signal currents, signal voltages, and signal powers.

The signal-handling capability of a transistor depends on how large the signal is. Even though the input-to-output signal relationship of a transistor is inherently nonlinear, a transistor can be adequately represented as a linear two-port device for very small signals. Large signals can cause the transistor to enter cutoff and saturation regions. Therefore, it is usual to assign certain small-signal parameters to the transistor when it is considered to be a linear two-port network.

Several sets of small-signal parameters are possible for the transistor two-port, represented in Fig. 1-2, depending on which of the signal voltages and currents are considered to be the independent variables and which are considered dependent variables. The voltages and currents can be expressed as phasors and the parameters as functions of frequency for small-signal sinusoids or everything can be expressed in terms of Laplace transforms.

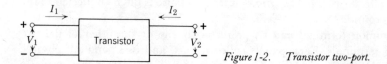

Figure 1-2.   Transistor two-port.

The parameter sets are summarized in Table 1-1, in which Φ_{i1} and Φ_{i2} represent the two independent quantities, Φ_{d1} and Φ_{d2} represent the two dependent quantities, and k_i, k_r, k_f, and k_o represent the parameters in a particular set.

The relationship between the dependent variables, the independent variables, and the parameters can be expressed in matrix form as

$$\begin{bmatrix} \Phi_{d1} \\ \Phi_{d2} \end{bmatrix} = \begin{bmatrix} k_i & k_r \\ k_f & k_o \end{bmatrix} \begin{bmatrix} \Phi_{i1} \\ \Phi_{i2} \end{bmatrix} \tag{1}$$

or as

$$[\Phi_d] = [k][\Phi_i] \tag{2}$$

where $[\Phi_d]$ and $[\Phi_i]$ are column matrices and $[k]$ is the square parameter matrix.

TABLE 1-1

Φ_{i1}	Φ_{i2}	Φ_{d1}	Φ_{d2}	k_i	k_r	k_f	k_o
I_1	I_2	V_1	V_2	z_i	z_r	z_f	z_o
V_1	V_2	I_1	I_2	y_i	y_r	y_f	y_o
I_1	V_2	V_1	I_2	h_i	h_r	h_f	h_o
V_1	I_2	I_1	V_2	g_i	g_r	g_f	g_o
V_2	$-I_2$	V_1	I_1	A	B	C	D
V_1	$-I_1$	V_2	I_2	$\mathcal{A}$	$\mathcal{B}$	$\mathcal{C}$	$\mathcal{D}$

Only three of the six parameter sets in Table 1-1 have been used extensively to describe two-port transistor circuits. These are the z, y, and h parameters. Scattering parameters, not given in Table 1-1 because they are related to voltages and currents indirectly, are becoming increasingly useful above about 100 MHz. An extensive treatment of scattering parameters is given in Chapter 6.

1-11 Open-Circuit Impedance Parameters [z]

If the currents are the independent variables, the dependent voltages are given by

$$\begin{bmatrix} V_1 \\ V_2 \end{bmatrix} = \begin{bmatrix} z_i & z_r \\ z_f & z_o \end{bmatrix} \begin{bmatrix} I_1 \\ I_2 \end{bmatrix} \tag{3}$$

or

$$V_1 = z_i I_1 + z_r I_2$$
$$V_2 = z_f I_1 + z_o I_2 \tag{4}$$

The z parameters are constants for a particular transistor and are determined at its operating point with a certain signal frequency. They are independent of signal amplitudes provided the amplitudes are small enough to insure linear operation. This constancy allows measurements to be made when one or the other independent current is set equal to zero.

The value of z_i may be found by opening the output circuit to make the *signal* current $I_2 = 0$ and then determining the current I_1 produced by a signal voltage V_1. Then $z_i = V_1/I_1$, and it is called the open-circuit input impedance. If the voltage V_2 produced at the open output terminals by the signal current I_1 is determined, then $z_f = V_2/I_1$, and it is called the open-circuit forward-direction transfer impedance.

Similarly, the value of z_r may be found by opening the input circuit to make the *signal* current $I_1 = 0$ and then determining the voltage V_1 produced at the open input terminals by a signal current I_2. Then $z_r = V_1/I_2$, and it is called the open-circuit reverse-direction transfer impedance. If the voltage V_2 produced at the output terminals by the current I_2 is determined, then $z_o = V_2/I_2$, and it is called the open-circuit output impedance.

Laboratory measurements of open-circuit impedance parameters require open circuits for the *signal* currents, not the DC currents. The transistor must still be biased properly. Effectively, an open circuit for signal current is obtained by inserting a large inductance in series with the circuit to be opened. This technique is adequate if the circuit impedance is already small before the inductance is added, but this condition is hardly satisfied for a reverse-biased collector-base junction. However, it is more nearly satisfied for a forward-biased emitter-base junction. Obtaining accurate measurements of the open-circuit impedance parameters over a wide frequency range can present some formidable problems.

The open-circuit impedance parameters were used to some extent in the early days of transistor development. Signal frequencies up to a few megahertz only were encountered, and the parameters had small reactive components. Advances in transistor modeling and the availability of other parameters have made the open-circuit impedance parameters obsolete as transistor specifications.

1-12 Short-Circuit Admittance Parameters [y]

If the voltages are the independent variables, the dependent currents are given by

$$\begin{bmatrix} I_1 \\ I_2 \end{bmatrix} = \begin{bmatrix} y_i & y_r \\ y_f & y_o \end{bmatrix} \begin{bmatrix} V_1 \\ V_2 \end{bmatrix} \tag{5}$$

or

$$I_1 = y_i V_1 + y_r V_2$$
$$I_2 = y_f V_1 + y_o V_2 \tag{6}$$

where

$$y_i = \frac{I_1}{V_1}\bigg|_{V_2=0} = \text{short-circuit input admittance}$$

$$y_r = \frac{I_1}{V_2}\bigg|_{V_1=0} = \text{short-circuit reverse transfer admittance}$$

$$y_f = \frac{I_2}{V_1}\bigg|_{V_2=0} = \text{short-circuit forward transfer admittance}$$

$$y_o = \frac{I_2}{V_2}\bigg|_{V_1=0} = \text{short-circuit output admittance}$$

The admittance parameters may be real or complex numbers depending on the transistor type and the signal frequency. When making laboratory measurements of the admittance parameters, the short circuits required to make V_1 and V_2 equal to zero are effectively obtained by placing a large capacitance across the terminals in question. This technique is particularly effective if the circuit impedance is already high, such as for a reverse-biased collector-base circuit, but is not so good if the circuit impedance is low, such as for a forward-biased emitter-base circuit.

When measurements are to be made over a wide range of frequencies extending to several hundred megahertz, a broadband short circuit is difficult to obtain. At such high frequencies, tuning stubs adjusted to the proper lengths can provide the required short circuits. Each change in signal frequency requires readjusting the stub lengths. Precise measurements of the short-circuit admittance parameters are sometimes difficult and tedious to obtain, but the y parameters are quite useful. The y-parameter variations with frequency are sometimes specified by the transistor manufacturer.

1-13 Hybrid Parameters [h]

It has been pointed out that an open circuit is most effectively obtained in a circuit whose impedance is normally quite small, and that a short circuit is most effectively obtained in a circuit whose impedance is normally quite high. For the transistor, this means that for the CB and CE configurations, the impedance of the output port is high so that parameter measurements involving a short circuit at the output should be accurate, and the impedance of the input port is small so that parameter measurements involving an open circuit at the input should be accurate. These advantages can be achieved using a set of hybrid parameters.

If I_1 and V_2 are selected to be the independent variables, then the dependent variables V_1 and I_2 are given by

$$\begin{bmatrix} V_1 \\ I_2 \end{bmatrix} = \begin{bmatrix} h_i & h_r \\ h_f & h_o \end{bmatrix} \begin{bmatrix} I_1 \\ V_2 \end{bmatrix} \tag{7}$$

or

$$V_1 = h_i I_1 + h_r V_2$$

$$I_2 = h_f I_1 + h_o V_2 \tag{8}$$

where

$$h_i = \frac{V_1}{I_1}\bigg|_{V_2=0} = \text{short-circuit input impedance}$$

$$h_r = \frac{V_1}{V_2}\bigg|_{I_1=0} = \text{open-circuit reverse voltage gain}$$

$$h_f = \frac{I_2}{I_1}\bigg|_{V_2=0} = \text{short-circuit forward current gain}$$

$$h_o = \frac{I_2}{V_2}\bigg|_{I_1=0} = \text{open-circuit output admittance}$$

These are called hybrid-h parameters because they all have different dimensions. For the CB and CE transistor configurations, the required short circuit that makes $V_2=0$ occurs in the high-impedance collector or output circuit and the required open circuit that makes $I_1=0$ occurs in the low-impedance emitter-base or input circuit. The hybrid-g and $ABCD$ parameters do not satisfy these circuit-impedance conditions, and have not been widely used as transistor specifications.

The h parameters may be real or complex numbers depending on the transistor and signal frequency. However, there is no standard and convenient notation for identifying the real and imaginary parts because of the different dimensions. The z parameters are conveniently represented by $r+jx$ because z, r, and x are all measured in ohms. The y parameters are conveniently represented by $g+jb$ because y, g, and b are all measured in mhos. About the best that can be done with the h parameters in this regard is to represent their parts by Re and Im, where Re and Im stand for "real part of" and "imaginary part of," respectively.

The h parameters are one of the most widely used parameter sets. Conversions between the z, y, and h parameters are given in Table 1-2.

TABLE 1-2 CONVERSIONS BETWEEN PARAMETERS*

From To	z		y		h	
z	z_i	z_r	$\dfrac{y_o}{D_y}$	$\dfrac{-y_r}{D_y}$	$\dfrac{D_h}{h_o}$	$\dfrac{h_r}{h_o}$
	z_f	z_o	$\dfrac{-y_f}{D_y}$	$\dfrac{y_i}{D_y}$	$\dfrac{-h_f}{h_o}$	$\dfrac{1}{h_o}$
y	$\dfrac{z_o}{D_z}$	$\dfrac{-z_r}{D_z}$	y_i	y_r	$\dfrac{1}{h_i}$	$\dfrac{-h_r}{h_i}$
	$\dfrac{-z_f}{D_z}$	$\dfrac{z_i}{D_z}$	y_f	y_o	$\dfrac{h_f}{h_i}$	$\dfrac{D_h}{h_i}$
h	$\dfrac{D_z}{z_o}$	$\dfrac{z_r}{z_o}$	$\dfrac{1}{y_i}$	$\dfrac{-y_r}{y_i}$	h_i	h_r
	$\dfrac{-z_f}{z_o}$	$\dfrac{1}{z_o}$	$\dfrac{y_f}{y_i}$	$\dfrac{D_y}{y_i}$	h_f	h_o

*D represents the value of the determinant formed by the parameters, for example, $D_h = h_i h_o - h_r h_f$.

1-2 INDEFINITE ADMITTANCE MATRIX

It is not absolutely essential for either the emitter, base, or collector of the transistor to be the common reference terminal. It is entirely appropriate to select some other external point as the common reference terminal as shown in Fig. 1-3. The terminals 1, 2, and 3 correspond to the base, emitter, and collector. The entire circuit acts like a three-port network. If the signal voltages are the independent variables, the dependent currents are given by

$$
\begin{bmatrix} I_1 \\ I_2 \\ I_3 \end{bmatrix} = \begin{bmatrix} y_{11} & y_{12} & y_{13} \\ y_{21} & y_{22} & y_{23} \\ y_{31} & y_{32} & y_{33} \end{bmatrix} \begin{bmatrix} V_1 \\ V_2 \\ V_3 \end{bmatrix} \tag{9}
$$

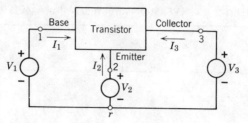

Figure 1-3.   Transistor with external reference node r.

The indefinite admittance matrix is useful because the sum of any row and of any column equals zero.

To prove that the sum of any column equals zero, apply Kirchhoff's current law at reference node r in Fig. 1-3. Then

$$I_1 + I_2 + I_3 = 0 \tag{10}$$

Since (9) is valid for any small values of signal voltages, let $V_2 = V_3 = 0$. Then (9) becomes

$$I_1 = y_{11} V_1 \qquad I_2 = y_{21} V_1 \qquad I_3 = y_{31} V_1 \tag{11}$$

Substitute (11) into (10) to obtain

$$(y_{11} + y_{21} + y_{31}) V_1 = 0 \tag{12}$$

Since V_1 was not assumed zero, then

$$y_{11} + y_{21} + y_{31} = 0 \tag{13}$$

which proves that the sum of the first column equals zero. Similarly, for the second column let $V_2 \neq 0$ with $V_1 = V_3 = 0$, and for the third column let $V_3 \neq 0$ with $V_1 = V_2 = 0$.

To prove that the sum of any row equals zero, let all three signal voltages be equal to V_o. Since all transistor terminals are at the same voltage relative to node r, there can be no current. Hence, for $V_1 = V_2 = V_3 = V_o$, the currents $I_1 = I_2 = I_3 = 0$. From (9),

$$I_1 = y_{11} V_1 + y_{12} V_2 + y_{13} V_3$$

or

$$0 = (y_{11} + y_{12} + y_{13}) V_o \tag{14}$$

Since V_o was not assumed zero, then

$$y_{11} + y_{12} + y_{13} = 0 \tag{15}$$

or, the sum of the first row equals zero. Writing the equations for I_2 and I_3 from (9) shows similarly that the sum of the second and third rows each equals zero.

If four of the nine parameters of the indefinite admittance matrix are known (but three of which are not in the same row or column), the others can be calculated to make the sum of any row and of any column equal to zero. This means that measurements can be made for transistor configurations which are most convenient and for which the required signal short-circuits are in normally high-impedance circuits.

Suppose the four short-circuit admittance parameters are known for the CE configuration. After calculating the other five parameters, they are arranged in the indefinite admittance matrix with the numbers entered in each row and column in this order: base, emitter, and collector. Then the y parameters for the CB configuration are found by the numbers remaining after crossing out row and column corresponding to the base numbers. The y parameters for the CC configuration are found by the numbers remaining after crossing out row and column corresponding to the collector numbers.

Example 1-1

The CE y parameters for a transistor are

$$y_{ie} = (2+j2) \times 10^{-3} \qquad y_{re} = (-2-j20) \times 10^{-6}$$

$$y_{fe} = (20-j3) \times 10^{-3} \qquad y_{oe} = (20+j60) \times 10^{-6}$$

Determine the CB and CC parameters.

Solution

The given parameters are inserted into the proper spaces of the indefinite admittance matrix after imagining crossing out row and column corresponding to the emitter as illustrated in Fig. 1-4a. Then calculate the other five parameters as shown in Fig. 1-4b. The CB parameters are $y_{ib} = (22.018 - j0.96) \times 10^{-3}$, $y_{rb} = (-18-j40) \times 10^{-6}$, $y_{fb} = (-20.02+j2.94) \times 10^{-3}$, $y_{ob} = (20+j60) \times 10^{-6}$. The CC or emitter follower parameters, are $y_{ic} = (2+j2) \times 10^{-3}$, $y_{rc} = (-1.998-j1.98) \times 10^{-3}$, $y_{fc} = (-22+j1) \times 10^{-3}$, $y_{oc} = (22.018-j0.96) \times 10^{-3}$.

Example 1-2

The CE y parameters for a transistor are the same as given in Example 1-1. Determine the CB h parameters.

	Base	Emitter	Collector
Base	$(2+j2)10^{-3}$		$(-2-j20)10^{-6}$
Emitter			
Collector	$(20-j3)10^{-3}$		$(20+j60)10^{-6}$

(a)

	Base	Emitter	Collector
Base	$(2+j2)10^{-3}$	$(-1.998-j1.98)10^{-3}$	$(-2-j20)10^{-6}$
Emitter	$(-22+j)10^{-3}$	$(22.018-j0.96)10^{-3}$	$(-18-j40)10^{-6}$
Collector	$(20-j3)10^{-3}$	$(-20.02+j2.94)10^{-3}$	$(20+j60)10^{-6}$

(b)

Figure 1-4. (a) CE y parameters inserted into the indefinite admittance matrix (b) other five parameters calculated from sum of any row and of any column equals zero.

Solution

Use the indefinite admittance matrix to find the CB y parameters as in Example 1-1. Then substitute into the relationships given in Table 1-2 to convert from CB y parameters to CB h parameters. The results are

$$h_{ib} = \frac{1}{y_{ib}} = 45.4 + j1.98$$

$$h_{rb} = \frac{-y_{rb}}{y_{ib}} = (-y_{rb})\left(\frac{1}{y_{ib}}\right) = (0.738 + j1.85)10^{-3}$$

$$h_{fb} = \frac{y_{fb}}{y_{ib}} = (y_{fb})\left(\frac{1}{y_{ib}}\right) = (-0.915 + j0.094)$$

$$h_{ob} = \frac{D_{yb}}{y_{ib}} = (y_{ib}y_{ob} - y_{rb}y_{fb})\left(\frac{1}{y_{ib}}\right)$$

$$= (0.020 + j0.554)(10^{-6})(45.4 + j1.98)$$

$$= (-0.192 + j25.2)10^{-6}$$

1-3 CALCULUS OF DEVIATIONS

In general, calculus is a word that means a mathematical system involving calculations. Therefore, the calculus of deviations is a system of definitions, rules, and procedures that relate to the change or deviation of one variable with respect to another. In the transistor, the presence of a signal causes the voltages and currents of the transistor to change or deviate around the bias point. Therefore, the amplitudes of the signal components represent the deviations of the voltages and currents.

Deviation notation can be illustrated using the parameter $y_i = I_1 / V_1$ with $V_2 = 0$. Thus y_i is equal to the small deviation in i_1 divided by the small deviation in v_1 when there is no deviation in v_2. This can be represented as

$$y_i = \frac{(i_1, v_2)}{(v_1, v_2)} \tag{16}$$

where the numerator means the deviation of i_1 with no deviation of v_2 and the denominator means the deviation of v_1 with no deviation of v_2. Similarly, since

$$z_i = \frac{V_1}{I_1}\bigg|_{I_2 = 0} \tag{17}$$

this can be written as

$$z_i = \frac{(v_1, i_2)}{(i_1, i_2)} \tag{18}$$

Since there are so many different parameters, it simplifies things to provide certain symbols for each of the deviation notations. These may be selected as follows:

Deviation	Symbol
(v_2, i_2)	A
(i_1, v_1)	B
(v_1, i_2)	G
(i_1, v_2)	H
(v_1, v_2)	Y
(i_1, i_2)	Z

Therefore $y_i = H / Y$ and $z_i = G / Z$.

1-31 Calculus-of-Deviations Rules

a. Association: $(i_1, v_1) + (i_1, v_2) = (i_1, v_1 + v_2)$
b. Commutation: $(v_1, v_2) = -(v_2, v_1)$
c. Multiplication: $(v_1, Cv_2) = (Cv_1, v_2) = C(v_1, v_2)$ where C is an arbitrary constant
d. Deviation zero: $(v_1, v_1) = 0$; $(v_1, C) = 0$

The deviations are not all independent of each other. It can be shown that

$$AB - GH + YZ = 0 \tag{19}$$

Table 1-3 shows the small-signal parameters represented in terms of the deviation symbols. The determinants are found using (19), for example,

$$D_h = h_i h_o - h_r h_f = \left(\frac{Y}{H}\right)\left(\frac{Z}{H}\right) - \left(\frac{B}{H}\right)\left(-\frac{A}{H}\right)$$

$$= \frac{YZ + AB}{H^2} = \frac{GH}{H^2} = \frac{G}{H}$$

TABLE 1-3 DEVIATION REPRESENTATION OF PARAMETERS

Parameters	Subscripts				Determinant
	i	r	f	o	
z	$\dfrac{G}{Z}$	$\dfrac{B}{Z}$	$\dfrac{A}{Z}$	$\dfrac{H}{Z}$	$D_z = \dfrac{Y}{Z}$
y	$\dfrac{H}{Y}$	$\dfrac{-B}{Y}$	$\dfrac{-A}{Y}$	$\dfrac{G}{Y}$	$D_y = \dfrac{Z}{Y}$
h	$\dfrac{Y}{H}$	$\dfrac{B}{H}$	$\dfrac{-A}{H}$	$\dfrac{Z}{H}$	$D_h = \dfrac{G}{H}$

Example 1-3

Given the common-base h parameters

$$h_{ib} = 50 \ \Omega \qquad h_{rb} = 5 \times 10^{-5}$$

$$h_{fb} = -0.99 \qquad h_{ob} = 1 \times 10^{-6} \ mho$$

Evaluate the deviations.

Solution

If CB parameters are specified, all of the deviations in Table 1-3 have an additional subscript B. This distinguishes CB deviations from CE and CC deviations, which use subscripts E and C, respectively.

Any one of the deviations in a parameter set can be arbitrary assigned the value unity. Since H is common to all denominators for the h deviations, it is convenient in this case to let $H=1$. From Table 1-3,

$$h_{ib} = Y_B = 50\ \Omega$$

$$h_{rb} = B_B = 5\times 10^{-5}$$

$$h_{fb} = -A_B = -0.99, \qquad \text{or}\ A_B = 0.99$$

$$h_{ob} = Z_B = 1\times 10^{-6}\ mho$$

$$D_{hb} = G_B = A_B B_B + Y_B Z_B = (0.99)(5\times 10^{-5}) + (50)(10^{-6})$$

$$= 9.95\times 10^{-5}$$

1-32 Transistor Parameter Conversions

One of the applications of the calculus of deviations is calculating any of the parameter sets for a circuit whose common terminal is different from the one for which the parameters were given. This requires another set of conversion relationships, but it provides an interesting alternative to converting the parameters with the aid of the indefinite admittance matrix.

Consider the transistor configurations of Fig. 1-5. The transistors are all biased at the same operating point. The signal currents and signal voltages have the same amplitudes, and only the current directions and voltage polarities vary from one circuit to another.

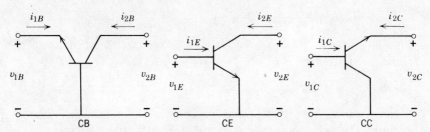

Figure 1-5.   Transistor configuration rotation.

The CB voltages and currents are related to those of the CE circuit by

$$v_{1B} = -v_{1E} \qquad v_{2B} = v_{2E} - v_{1E}$$

$$i_{1B} = -(i_{1E} + i_{2E}) \qquad i_{2B} = i_{2E} \tag{20}$$

The CE circuit is related to the CC circuit by

$$v_{1E} = v_{1C} - v_{2C} \qquad v_{2E} = -v_{2C}$$

$$i_{1E} = i_{1C} \qquad i_{2E} = -(i_{1C} + i_{2C})$$

(21)

Finally, CB relates to CC by

$$v_{1B} = v_{2C} - v_{1C} \qquad v_{2B} = -v_{1C}$$

$$i_{1B} = i_{2C} \qquad i_{2B} = -(i_{1C} + i_{2C})$$

(22)

The technique of using these relationships is illustrated below in deriving CB deviations from CE deviations.

$$A_B = (v_{2B}, i_{2B}) = (v_{2E} - v_{1E}, i_{2E}) = (v_{2E}, i_{2E}) - (v_{1E}, i_{2E})$$
$$= A_E - G_E$$
$$B_B = (i_{1B}, v_{1B}) = (-i_{1E} - i_{2E}, -v_{1E}) = (-i_{1E}, -v_{1E}) + (-i_{2E}, v_{1E})$$
$$= B_E - G_E$$
$$G_B = (v_{1B}, i_{2B}) = (-v_{1E}, i_{2E}) = -(v_{1E}, i_{2E}) = -G_E$$
$$H_B = (i_{1B}, v_{2B}) = (-i_{1E} - i_{2E}, v_{2E} - v_{1E})$$
$$= (-i_{1E}, v_{2E}) + (-i_{1E}, -v_{1E}) + (-i_{2E}, v_{2E}) + (-i_{2E}, -v_{1E})$$
$$= -H_E + B_E + A_E - G_E = F_E$$
$$Y_B = (v_{1B}, v_{2B}) = (-v_{1E}, v_{2E} - v_{1E}) = (-v_{1E}, v_{2E}) = -Y_E$$
$$Z_B = (i_{1B}, i_{2B}) = (-i_{1E} - i_{2E}, i_{2E}) = (-i_{1E}, i_{2E}) = -Z_E$$

A similar procedure is followed to obtain the other conversion relationships. The deviation conversions are given in Table 1-4. Note that an auxiliary deviation F has been defined given by

$$F = A + B - G - H$$

(23)

Example 1-4

Given the CB h parameters of Example 1-3. Calculate the CC y parameters.

TABLE 1-4 DEVIATION CONVERSIONS

From CB to

CE	CC
$A_E = A_B - G_B$	$A_C = -B_B + H_B$
$B_E = B_B - G_B$	$B_C = -A_B + H_B$
$G_E = -G_B$	$G_C = H_B$
$H_E = F_B$	$H_C = -F_B$
$Y_E = -Y_B$	$Y_C = Y_B$
$Z_E = -Z_B$	$Z_C = Z_B$
$F_E = H_B$	$F_C = -G_B$

From CE to

CB	CC
$A_B = A_E - G_E$	$A_C = A_E - H_E$
$B_B = B_E - G_E$	$B_C = B_E - H_E$
$G_B = -G_E$	$G_C = F_E$
$H_B = F_E$	$H_C = -H_E$
$Y_B = -Y_E$	$Y_C = -Y_E$
$Z_B = -Z_E$	$Z_C = -Z_E$
$F_B = H_E$	$F_C = G_E$

From CC to

CB	CE
$A_B = -B_C + G_C$	$A_E = A_C - H_C$
$B_B = -A_C + G_C$	$B_E = B_C - H_C$
$G_B = -F_C$	$G_E = F_C$
$H_B = G_C$	$H_E = -H_C$
$Y_B = Y_C$	$Y_E = -Y_C$
$Z_B = Z_C$	$Z_E = -Z_C$
$F_B = -H_C$	$F_E = G_C$

Solution

From Table 1-4, and substituting the CB deviations calculated in Example 1-3, the CC deviations are obtained as follows:

$$A_C = -B_B + H_B = -5 \times 10^{-5} + 1 = 0.99995$$
$$B_C = -A_B + H_B = -0.99 + 1 = 0.01$$
$$G_C = \quad H_B \qquad = 1$$
$$H_C = -F_B \qquad = G_B + H_B - A_B - B_B = 0.0100495$$
$$Y_C = \quad Y_B \qquad = 50$$
$$Z_C = \quad Z_B \qquad = 1 \times 10^{-6}$$
$$F_C = -G_B \qquad = -9.95 \times 10^{-5}$$

Next, substituting into the proper parameter set of Table 1-3, the CC y parameters are

$$y_{ic} = \frac{H_C}{Y_C} = \frac{0.0100495}{50} \cong 0.0002$$

$$y_{rc} = \frac{-B_C}{Y_C} = \frac{-0.01}{50} = -0.0002$$

$$y_{fc} = \frac{-A_C}{Y_C} = \frac{-0.99995}{50} \cong 0.02$$

$$y_{oc} = \frac{G_C}{Y_C} = \frac{1}{50} = 0.02$$

$$D_{yc} = \frac{Z_C}{Y_C} = \frac{1 \times 10^{-6}}{50} = 2 \times 10^{-8}$$

1-4 ACTIVITY AND PASSIVITY

Transistors are useful as amplifiers and oscillators as determined by their small-signal parameters. A circuit that can be made to amplify signal power or to oscillate is called an active circuit. Passive circuits cannot be made to amplify power or oscillate. Circuits composed of linear time-invariant resistors, inductors, or capacitors are passive circuits.

A transistor is passive when the total average small-signal power entering all ports is zero or positive. If zero, the circuit is lossless; if positive, the circuit is lossy. If the total power is negative, more power leaves one or more of the ports than enters, so the transistor is active. Whether or not the total power is nonnegative, that is, whether or not the transistor is passive, can be conveniently related to the small-signal parameters.

The total average signal power entering both ports is

$$P = |V_1||I_1|\cos\theta_1 + |V_2||I_2|\cos\theta_2$$

$$= \operatorname{Re} V_1 I_1^* + \operatorname{Re} V_2 I_2^*$$

$$= \operatorname{Re} V_1^* I_1 + \operatorname{Re} V_2^* I_2 \tag{24}$$

where superscript * denotes conjugate. Also

$$P = \tfrac{1}{2}(V_1^* I_1 + I_1^* V_1) + \tfrac{1}{2}(V_2^* I_2 + I_2^* V_2)$$

Rearrange terms to obtain

$$P = \tfrac{1}{2}(V_1^* I_1 + V_2^* I_2) + \tfrac{1}{2}(I_1^* V_1 + I_2^* V_2) \tag{25}$$

or, in matrix form,

$$P = \tfrac{1}{2}[V^*]^t[I] + \tfrac{1}{2}[I^*]^t[V] \tag{26}$$

where superscript t denotes transpose. Since

$$[I] = [y][V] \qquad \text{and} \qquad [I^*]^t = [V^*]^t[y^*]^t \tag{27}$$

then

$$P = \tfrac{1}{2}[V^*]^t[y][V] + \tfrac{1}{2}[V^*]^t[y^*]^t[V] \tag{28}$$

which factors to give

$$P = [V^*]^t \left\{ \tfrac{1}{2}([y] + [y^*]^t) \right\}[V] \tag{29}$$

$$= [V^*]^t[y_H][V] \tag{30}$$

where

$$[y_H] = \tfrac{1}{2}([y] + [y^*]^t) \tag{31}$$

The matrix $[y_H]$ is called hermitian. A matrix is hermitian if its elements along the principal diagonal are real and if its elements symmetrically arranged each side of the principal diagonal are complex conjugates. The matrix $[y_H]$ satisfies these requirements.

The particular arrangement of matrices in (30) is called the hermitian form for the power P. For passivity, the power $P \geqslant 0$ for all $V \neq 0$, and the hermitian form is said to be positive-semidefinite. In order for the hermitian form to be positive-semidefinite, the determinant value of $[y_H]$ and that of each of its principal minors must be nonnegative. The principal minors are the determinants formed by the first, the first two, the first three, etc. rows and columns of a determinant. Therefore, the criteria for passivity can be expressed by the admittance parameters because they determine the elements of $[y_H]$. If any of the passivity conditions are violated, the transistor is an active device.

Let the y parameters be given by

$$[y] = \begin{bmatrix} g_i + jb_i & g_r + jb_r \\ g_f + jb_f & g_o + jb_o \end{bmatrix} \tag{32}$$

To form the hermitian admittance matrix, $[y^*]^t$ is also needed. Thus,

$$[y^*] = \begin{bmatrix} g_i - jb_i & g_r - jb_r \\ g_f - jb_f & g_o - jb_o \end{bmatrix} \tag{33}$$

The transpose is formed by interchanging the rows and columns of (33). Thus,

$$[y^*]^t = \begin{bmatrix} g_i - jb_i & g_f - jb_f \\ g_r - jb_r & g_o - jb_o \end{bmatrix} \tag{34}$$

Next, add (32) and (34) and divide by 2.

$$[y_H] = \tfrac{1}{2}([y] + [y^*]^t) = \begin{bmatrix} g_i & \dfrac{y_r + y_f^*}{2} \\ \dfrac{y_f + y_r^*}{2} & g_o \end{bmatrix} \tag{35}$$

For the transistor to be passive, the determinant value of $[y_H]$ and each of its principal minors must be nonnegative. This means that

$$g_i \geqslant 0 \tag{36a}$$

and that

$$g_i g_o - \frac{y_r + y_f^*}{2} \frac{y_f + y_r^*}{2} \geqslant 0 \tag{36b}$$

Inequality (36b) simplifies to the alternate forms

$$g_i g_o - g_r g_f - \frac{|y_f - y_r|^2}{4} \geqslant 0 \tag{37a}$$

and

$$g_i g_o + b_r b_f - \frac{|y_f + y_r|^2}{4} \geqslant 0 \tag{37b}$$

Interchanging input and output ports also indicates that, for passivity,

$$g_o \geqslant 0 \tag{38}$$

If any one of the conditions given by (36), (37), and (38) is not satisfied, the transistor is active instead of passive.

Example   1-5

Determine whether the transistor whose CE y parameters are given in Example 1.1 is active or passive.

Solution

$$g_{ie} = 2 \times 10^{-3} > 0$$

$$g_{oe} = 20 \times 10^{-6} > 0$$

$$g_{ie} g_{oe} - g_{re} g_{fe} - \frac{|y_{fe} - y_{re}|^2}{4} \cong -100 \times 10^{-6} \not> 0$$

Since one of the passivity conditions is violated, the transistor is active at the operating point and frequency for which the parameters apply.

The passivity condition (37a) can be rewritten as

$$1 - \frac{|y_f - y_r|^2}{4(g_i g_o - g_r g_f)} \geqslant 0 \tag{39}$$

or as

$$1 - U \geqslant 0 \tag{40}$$

where

$$U = \frac{|y_f - y_r|^2}{4(g_i g_o - g_r g_f)} \tag{41}$$

Thus if $g_i \geqslant 0$ and $g_o \geqslant 0$, and $0 \leqslant U \leqslant 1$, the transistor is passive. If $U > 1$, the transistor is active. Hence U is a measure of the "degree" of activity. In Example 1-5, $U \cong 1270$.

When $U > 1$, the transistor can deliver more signal power output than it receives as signal power input. Therefore some of the output power can be fed back to provide the input power. This means that the transistor can be used as an oscillator so long as $U > 1$. However, U depends on frequency because the y parameters vary with frequency. Generally, $U(\omega) > 1$ at low frequencies and decreases as the frequency is increased. There is a frequency ω_{max} for which $U(\omega_{max}) = 1$. Above this frequency, $U(\omega) < 1$ so that oscillation is impossible. Therefore, ω_{max} is called "maximum frequency of oscillation."

In terms of the generalized k parameters, it is found that the passivity criteria have exactly the same form as (36), (37), and (38), with the real and imaginary parts of the generalized parameters replacing corresponding real and imaginary parts of the y parameters.

Thus, for passivity,

$$\operatorname{Re} k_i \geqslant 0 \tag{42}$$

$$\operatorname{Re} k_o \geqslant 0 \tag{43}$$

and

$$\operatorname{Re} k_i \operatorname{Re} k_o - \operatorname{Re} k_r \operatorname{Re} k_f - \frac{|k_f - k_r|^2}{4} \geqslant 0 \tag{44a}$$

or, alternatively,

$$\operatorname{Re} k_i \operatorname{Re} k_o + \operatorname{Im} k_r \operatorname{Im} k_f - \frac{|k_f + k_r|^2}{4} \geqslant 0 \tag{44b}$$

1-5 THE HYBRID-π TRANSISTOR MODEL

The h and y parameters are very strongly dependent on the type of transistor, DC bias conditions, temperature, and frequency of operation. Therefore, the parameters must be given for a certain set of operating conditions. Sometimes the parameters are presented graphically as functions of collector current, temperature, and frequency.

Some of the frequency dependent data could be eliminated by specifying the components for the hybrid-π transistor model shown in Fig. 1-6, for certain bias conditions. One of the main advantages of the hybrid-π model is that the various components are nearly constant for all frequencies up to about the alpha-cutoff frequency. Typical values are shown in Fig. 1-6. In the actual transistor, three additional capacitors appear, one between each pair of terminals. The values of these capacitors depend on the transistor design and how it is packaged, but they are generally rather small. At low frequencies their effects are negligible.

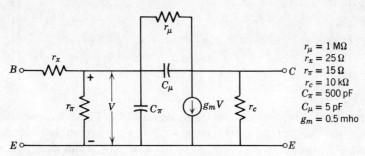

$r_\mu = 1\ \text{M}\Omega$
$r_x = 25\ \Omega$
$r_\pi = 15\ \Omega$
$r_c = 10\ \text{k}\Omega$
$C_\pi = 500\ \text{pF}$
$C_\mu = 5\ \text{pF}$
$g_m = 0.5\ \text{mho}$

Figure 1-6.   The hybrid-π model and typical values.

1-51 Hybrid-π Model Simplifications

The hybrid-π model can be simplified somewhat after determining the contribution of each resistor-capacitor parallel combination. There is a frequency for which r_μ equals the reactance of C_μ. This frequency is, for the typical values given,

$$\frac{1}{2\pi r_\mu C_\mu} = \frac{1}{2\pi(10^6)(5 \times 10^{-12})} \cong 32\ \text{kHz} \qquad (45)$$

At frequencies considerably below 32 kHz, the reactance of C_μ is much larger than r_μ, so r_μ dominates and C_μ can be omitted. At frequencies considerably above 32 kHz, the reactance of C_μ is much less than r_μ, so C_μ dominates and r_μ can be neglected.

Similarly, for r_π and C_π, the frequency

$$\frac{1}{2\pi r_\pi C_\pi} = \frac{1}{2\pi(15)(500 \times 10^{-12})} \cong 21\ \text{MHz} \qquad (46)$$

makes the reactance of C_π equal to r_π. Therefore at frequencies much below 21 MHz, C_π can be neglected, and at frequencies much larger than this, r_π

can be neglected. The simplified model to be used depends on the frequency range to be considered.

1-52 Hybrid-π Indefinite Admittance Matrix

A general circuit similar to the hybrid-π is shown in Fig. 1-7. The four terminal currents are related to the terminal voltages with respect to an external reference point and the indefinite admittance matrix by

$$
\begin{bmatrix} I_1 \\ I_2 \\ I_3 \\ I_4 \end{bmatrix} = \begin{bmatrix} Y_a & 0 & 0 & -Y_a \\ 0 & (Y_b + Y_c + Y_f) & -Y_c & -(Y_b + Y_f) \\ 0 & -(Y_f + Y_c) & (Y_c + Y_d) & (Y_f - Y_d) \\ -Y_a & -Y_b & -Y_d & (Y_a + Y_b + Y_d) \end{bmatrix} \begin{bmatrix} V_1 \\ V_2 \\ V_3 \\ V_4 \end{bmatrix}
$$

(47)

When used to represent a transistor, terminal 4 in Fig. 1-7 is not accessible because the base spreading resistor r_x separates the accessible base terminal from the "intrinsic" base. Therefore I_4 must be zero in this case. From (47),

$$I_4 = 0 = -Y_a V_1 - Y_b V_2 - Y_d V_3 + (Y_a + Y_b + Y_d) V_4$$

so that

$$V_4 = \frac{-Y_a V_1 - Y_b V_2 - Y_d V_3}{Y_a + Y_b + Y_d}$$

(48)

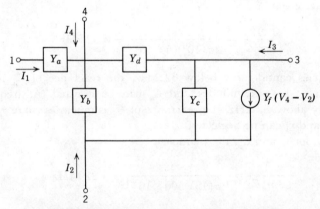

Figure 1-7. A general hybrid-π circuit in which terminal 1 corresponds to the base, 2 to the emitter, and 3 to the collector. Terminal 4 is not accessible in a transistor.

Setting $I_4 = 0$ and substituting (48) for V_4 in (47), then collecting terms, give the indefinite admittance matrix for the hybrid-π transistor model as

$$
\begin{array}{ccc}
 & b & e & c
\end{array}
$$

$$
\frac{1}{Y_a + Y_b + Y_d}
\begin{array}{c}
b \\ \\ e \\ \\ \\ c
\end{array}
\left[
\begin{array}{ccc}
Y_a(Y_b + Y_d) & -Y_a Y_b & -Y_a Y_d \\
& & \\
-Y_a(Y_b + Y_f) & (Y_a + Y_d)(Y_b + Y_f) & -Y_c(Y_a + Y_b + Y_d) \\
& +Y_c(Y_a + Y_b + Y_d) & -Y_d(Y_b + Y_f) \\
& & \\
Y_a(Y_f - Y_d) & -Y_a(Y_a + Y_b + Y_d) & Y_c(Y_a + Y_b + Y_d) \\
& -Y_d(Y_b + Y_f) & +Y_d(Y_a + Y_b + Y_f) \\
& -Y_a Y_f &
\end{array}
\right]
$$

$$(49)$$

When the components of the hybrid-π transistor model are known the short-circuit admittance parameters for any of the transistor configurations may be found from (49).

1-53 Maximum Frequency of Oscillation

The highest frequency ω_{max} for which the transistor is active may be found from $U(\omega_{max}) = 1$. As discussed in Section 1-51, at sufficiently high frequencies the hybrid-π model simplified into the one shown in Fig. 1-8. Comparing components in Figs. 1-7 and 1-8 shows that

$$
Y_a = \frac{1}{r_x} = g_x \qquad Y_b = j\omega C_\pi \qquad Y_c = \frac{1}{r_c} = g_c
$$

$$
Y_d = j\omega C_\mu \qquad Y_f = g_m \qquad V_4 - V_2 = V
$$

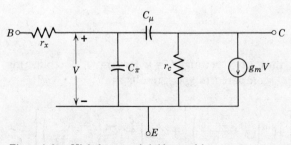

Figure 1-8.   High-frequency hybrid-π model.

From (49), the y parameters for the CE transistor are

$$[y] = \frac{\begin{bmatrix} g_x(j\omega)(C_\pi + C_\mu) & -g_x(j\omega C_\mu) \\ g_x(g_m - j\omega C_\mu) & g_c[g_x + j\omega(C_\pi + C_\mu)] \\ & +j\omega C_\mu(g_x + g_m + j\omega C_\pi) \end{bmatrix}}{g_x + j\omega(C_\pi + C_\mu)} \tag{50}$$

Since $C_\pi \gg C_\mu$, it is found that

$$g_i \cong \frac{\omega^2 g_x C_\pi^2}{g_x^2 + \omega^2 C_\pi^2} \tag{51}$$

which is always positive, and

$$g_o \cong g_c + \frac{\omega^2 g_m C_\pi C_\mu}{g_x^2 + \omega^2 C_\pi^2} \tag{52}$$

which is always positive, and

$$y_f \cong \frac{g_x(g_x g_m - \omega^2 C_\pi C_\mu) - j\omega(g_x g_m C_\pi + g_x^2 C_\mu)}{g_x^2 + \omega^2 C_\pi^2} \tag{53}$$

and

$$y_r \cong -\frac{\omega^2 g_x C_\pi C_\mu + j\omega g_x^2 C_\mu}{g_x^2 + \omega^2 C_\pi^2} \tag{54}$$

Therefore

$$\frac{|y_f - y_r|^2}{4} \cong \frac{g_m^2 g_x^2}{4(g_x^2 + \omega^2 C_\pi^2)} \tag{55}$$

Substituting into (41), setting $U = 1$ for $\omega = \omega_{max}$, collecting terms, and neglecting $g_x C_\mu$ compared to $g_m C_\pi$, results in

$$\omega_{max}^4 \left[4C_\pi^4 \left(g_c + \frac{g_m C_\mu}{C_\pi} \right) \right] + \omega_{max}^2 \left[4g_x^2 C_\pi^2 \left(g_c - \frac{g_m^2}{4g_x} \right) \right] - g_m^2 g_x^3 = 0 \tag{56}$$

Typical values are such that

$$g_c \ll \frac{g_m C_\mu}{C_\pi} \quad \text{and} \quad g_c \ll \frac{g_m^2}{g_x} \tag{57}$$

Therefore (56) becomes, subject to the inequalities (57),

$$\omega_{max}^4 + \omega_{max}^2 \left(-\frac{g_m g_x}{4 C_\pi C_\mu} \right) - \frac{g_x^3 g_m}{4 C_\pi^3 C_\mu} = 0 \tag{58}$$

Solving (58) for ω_{max}^2, using the quadratic formula, gives

$$\omega_{max}^2 = \frac{g_x g_m}{8 C_\pi C_\mu} \left(1 + \sqrt{1 + 16 g_x C_\mu / g_m C_\pi} \right) \tag{59}$$

Since typically $g_x C_\mu \gg g_m C_\pi$, the maximum frequency of oscillation is found from (59) to be

$$2\pi f_{max} = \omega_{max} \cong \sqrt{g_x g_m / 4 C_\pi C_\mu} \tag{60}$$

For frequencies above ω_{max}, the transistor is passive.

Using the typical values given in Fig. 1-6,

$$f_{max} \cong \frac{1}{2\pi} \sqrt{g_m / 4 r_x C_\pi C_\mu} = 225 \text{ MHz}$$

Other calculations show that

$$f_T = \frac{g_m}{2\pi C_\pi} = 159 \text{ MHz} \cong f_\alpha$$

and the low-frequency short-circuit current gain is

$$h_{fe} = g_m r_\pi = 7.5$$

so that

$$f_\beta = \frac{f_T}{h_{fe}} = \frac{1}{2\pi r_\pi C_\pi} = 21.2 \text{ MHz}$$

PROBLEMS

1-1. The CE y parameters for a transistor are

$$y_{ie} = (20 + j10)10^{-3} \qquad y_{re} = (-1 - j0.5)10^{-3}$$

$$y_{fe} = (40 - j100)10^{-3} \qquad y_{oe} = (1 + j5)10^{-3}$$

Determine the y parameters for the CB and CC configurations.

1-2. Starting with the CE y parameters of Problem 1-1, determine the CB h parameters by two methods and compare results.

1-3. Is the transistor of Problem 1-1 active or passive in each of the three configurations?

1-4. Use the rules and procedures of the calculus of deviations to show that the value of U obtained for the CE configuration of a transistor is the same value of U for either the CB or CC configurations of the same transistor.

1-5. Is the maximum frequency of oscillation influenced by the type of configuration, that is, by CB, CE, or CC?

CHAPTER TWO

STABILITY AND AMPLIFIER DESIGN

2-0 INTRODUCTION

When the parameters are such that the transistor is active, it is capable of power amplification and oscillation. In order to take advantage of this capability, the transistor must be connected into a circuit that provides terminating impedances at both input and output ports. For an amplifier, a signal source is also connected to the input port (Fig. 2-1). For such circuits, voltage, current, and power gains, and input and output impedances (or admittances) are usually of interest.

The input or output immittance (i.e., either impedance or admittance) requires special attention. This is because if the real part of the input or output immittance is negative, it is possible for the transistor to oscillate for certain terminating immittances. This oscillation can occur in some tuned amplifiers, where it can be an annoying problem. It can also occur when the parameters are being measured. For example, a stub used to provide a short circuit at the signal frequency can be highly reactive at another frequency for which the circuit oscillates and causes difficulty with the measurements.

Impedance and gain properties of a linear transistor circuit are given in Table 2-1.

Similarities between the input and output immittances allow them to be expressed in terms of the generalized k parameters. Thus

$$\Gamma_{\text{in}} = k_i - \frac{k_r k_f}{k_o + \Gamma_L} \tag{1}$$

27

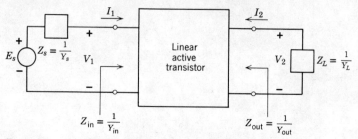

Figure 2-1. Linear active transistor with terminations at its two ports.

and

$$\Gamma_{\text{out}} = k_o - \frac{k_r k_f}{k_i + \Gamma_s} \tag{2}$$

where Γ_{in} and Γ_{out} are the input and output immittances defined in Table 2-2, and Γ_L and Γ_s are the terminating immittances also defined in Table 2-2.

For example, from Table 2-2, the input immittance $\Gamma_{\text{in}} = Y_{\text{in}}$ and the load immittance $\Gamma_L = Y_L$ when y parameters are used for the generalized k parameters in (1). Also, the output immittance $\Gamma_{\text{out}} = Y_{\text{out}}$ and the source immittance $\Gamma_s = Y_s$. Therefore,

$$Y_{\text{in}} = G_{\text{in}} + jB_{\text{in}} = y_i - \frac{y_r y_f}{y_o + Y_L} \tag{3}$$

and

$$Y_{\text{out}} = G_{\text{out}} + jB_{\text{out}} = y_o - \frac{y_r y_f}{y_i + Y_s} \tag{4}$$

TABLE 2-1 IMPEDANCE AND GAIN PROPERTIES

	$[z]$	$[y]$	$[h]$
Z_{in}	$\dfrac{D_z + z_i Z_L}{z_o + Z_L}$	$\dfrac{y_o + Y_L}{D_y + y_i Y_L}$	$\dfrac{D_h + h_i Y_L}{h_o + Y_L}$
Z_{out}	$\dfrac{D_z + z_o Z_s}{z_i + Z_s}$	$\dfrac{y_i + Y_s}{D_y + y_o Y_s}$	$\dfrac{h_i + Z_s}{D_h + h_o Z_s}$
$A_v = \dfrac{V_2}{V_1}$	$\dfrac{z_f Z_L}{D_z + z_i Z_L}$	$\dfrac{-y_f}{y_o + Y_L}$	$\dfrac{-h_f}{D_h + h_i Y_L}$
$A_i = \dfrac{I_2}{I_1}$	$\dfrac{-z_f}{z_o + Z_L}$	$\dfrac{y_f Y_L}{D_y + y_i Y_L}$	$\dfrac{h_f Y_L}{h_o + Y_L}$

TABLE 2-2 IMMITTANCES FOR SEVERAL PARAMETERS SETS

k	Γ_{in}	Γ_{out}	Γ_s	Γ_L
z	Z_{in}	Z_{out}	Z_s	Z_L
y	Y_{in}	Y_{out}	Y_s	Y_L
h	Z_{in}	Y_{out}	Z_s	Y_L

where G and B denote conductance and susceptance, respectively. If h parameters are used, then $\Gamma_{in} = Z_{in}$ and $\Gamma_L = Y_L$ in (1), and $\Gamma_{out} = Y_{out}$ and $\Gamma_s = Z_s$ in (2). Therefore,

$$Z_{in} = R_{in} + jX_{in} = h_i - \frac{h_r h_f}{h_o + Y_L} \tag{5}$$

and

$$Y_{out} = G_{out} + jB_{out} = h_o - \frac{h_r h_f}{h_i + Z_s} \tag{6}$$

where R and X denote resistance and reactance, respectively.

2-1 NATURE OF NEGATIVE RESISTANCE

Ohm's law defines the resistance of Fig. 2-2a as

$$r = \frac{V}{I} \tag{7}$$

and the resistance is positive and dissipates energy. If the voltage polarity is reversed (or if the current direction is reversed) as in Fig. 2-2b, the resistance is

$$r = -\frac{V}{I} \tag{8}$$

and the resistance is negative.

The ideal voltage source in Fig. 2-2c delivers energy to the external circuit when the current is in the direction shown. In this case the ratio $V/I = -r$, which can be substituted for the ideal voltage source as shown in Fig. 2-2d. Therefore a negative resistance acts as a source that delivers energy to the external circuit. Of course, a negative conductance acts the same way.

Consider the circuit in Fig. 2-2e. The current is

$$I = \frac{10}{150 - 50} = 0.1 \text{ A}$$

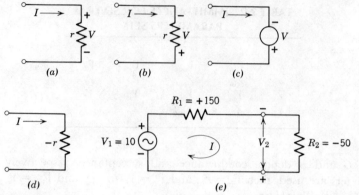

Figure 2-2. (a) $r = V/I$, (b) $r = -V/I$, (c) Ideal voltage source delivering energy to external circuit, (d) $-r = V/I$ substitutes for the ideal voltage source, (e) A circuit with negative resistance.

The power delivered by the 10-V source is

$$P_s = 10(0.1) = 1 \text{ W}$$

The power dissipated in R_1 (the positive resistance) is

$$P_{R_1} = (0.1)^2(150) = 1.5 \text{ W}$$

Since the power dissipated in R_1 is greater than P_s by 0.5 W, the additional 0.5 W must come from the negative resistance.

The voltage across R_2 (with the polarity indicated) is

$$V_2 = 0.1(50) = 5 \text{ V}$$

Therefore the power delivered by the negative resistance is

$$P_{R_2} = V_2 I = (0.1)^2(50) = 5(.1) = 0.5 \text{ W}$$

If the input conductance G_{in} of (3) is negative, the transistor delivers energy to the external input circuit. This energy is obtained ultimately from the DC bias source in the output circuit and is fed back to the input circuit through the transistor. If an RLC circuit is present at the input port, it is possible for the energy provided by the negative input conductance of the transistor to supply all the energy losses of the input circuit. When this occurs, a lossless LC input circuit is effectively obtained. Therefore, when the LC input circuit begins to oscillate, it continues to do so at a constant amplitude with the transistor supplying the input losses. The entire circuit is an oscillator, and external feedback need not be present.

2-2 STABILITY AND INSTABILITY

When oscillation occurs, the transistor amplifier circuit is said to be unstable. If the negative input conductance cannot provide all the losses for the particular passive input circuit used, sustained oscillation does not occur and the transistor circuit is stable and may act as an amplifier. It is potentially unstable, however, because a different passive input circuit may allow oscillation. When no combination of input and output admittances makes either the input or output conductances negative, the transistor is said to be inherently, unconditionally, or absolutely stable. The only way to use an inherently stable transistor as an oscillator is to provide suitable external feedback.

Passive circuits are inherently stable with positive input and output conductances, but inherently stable circuits are not necessarily passive; they may be active. Potentially unstable circuits are always active, but the converse is not true because an active circuit can be inherently stable.

2-3 CONDITIONS FOR INHERENT STABILITY

Starting with (3) and allowing the load admittance and the y parameters to be complex numbers, the input conductance G_{in} will be determined. Then G_{in} will be minimized by choice of the passive load admittance Y_L, and the condition that makes $(G_{in})_{min}$ greater than zero will be found.

The input admittance is

$$Y_{in} = G_{in} + jB_{in} = y_i - \frac{y_r y_f}{y_o + Y_L} \tag{9}$$

Let

$$y_i = g_i + jb_i \tag{10}$$

$$y_o = g_o + jb_o \tag{11}$$

$$y_r y_f = P + jQ = M \underline{/\theta} \tag{12}$$

$$Y_L = G_L + jB_L \tag{13}$$

The input conductance is found to be

$$G_{in} = g_i - \frac{P(g_o + G_L) + Q(b_o + B_L)}{(g_o + G_L)^2 + (b_o + B_L)^2} \tag{14}$$

which can be written as (for $g_i \neq 0$)

$$G_{in} = \frac{(g_o + G_L)^2 + (b_o + B_L)^2 - \dfrac{P}{g_i}(g_o + G_L) - \dfrac{Q}{g_i}(b_o + B_L)}{\dfrac{1}{g_i}\left[(g_o + G_L)^2 + (b_o + B_L)^2\right]} \quad (15)$$

The denominator of (15) is always positive for inherent stability, because if $g_i < 0$ the circuit can oscillate for a shorted load. In the case $g_i = 0$, oscillation occurs for a shorted load if a lossless LC circuit is connected to the input port. Therefore only the numerator of (15) need be used to determine the sign of G_{in}.

After rearranging the terms, adding and subtracting $(P^2 + Q^2)/4g_i^2$, and simplifying, the numerator of (15) becomes

$$N = \left[G_L + \left(g_o - \frac{P}{2g_i}\right)\right]^2 + \left[B_L + \left(b_o - \frac{Q}{2g_i}\right)\right]^2 - \frac{P^2 + Q^2}{4g_i^2} \quad (16)$$

The load admittance that minimizes (16) also minimizes the input conductance G_{in}. The first two terms of (16) are always positive, and each is minimized independent of the other by choosing G_L and B_L. The first term is minimized by setting $G_L = 0$, since negative load conductances cannot be obtained with passive elements. The second term has a minimum value of zero when

$$B_L = -\left(b_o - \frac{Q}{2g_i}\right) \quad (17)$$

Load susceptances of either sign may be obtained with passive elements. Therefore the minimum value of N is

$$N_{min} = \left(g_o - \frac{P}{2g_i}\right)^2 - \frac{P^2 + Q^2}{4g_i^2} \quad (18)$$

In order for $(G_{in})_{min} > 0$, $N_{min} > 0$. Therefore

$$\left(g_o - \frac{P}{2g_i}\right)^2 - \frac{P^2 + Q^2}{4g_i^2} > 0 \quad (19)$$

or simplifying,

$$g_i g_o > \frac{P + \sqrt{P^2 + Q^2}}{2} \quad (20)$$

This is also expressed in alternative form as

$$g_i g_o > \frac{M}{2}(1 + \cos\theta) \tag{21}$$

Inequality (20) or (21) is the desired condition that was sought.

The conditions for inherent stability are summarized below. At any frequency for which the y parameters are determined,

$$g_i > 0 \qquad g_o > 0 \tag{22}$$

and

$$g_i g_o > \frac{P + M}{2} \tag{23a}$$

or

$$g_i g_o > \frac{M}{2}(1 + \cos\theta) \tag{23b}$$

The circuit is inherently stable if all inequalities in (22) and (23) are satisfied. If any one of the inequalities is not satisfied, the circuit is potentially unstable.

Exactly the same conditions are obtained if the output admittance given by (4) is used as a starting point instead of the input admittance.

Example 2-1

Determine the stability of the transistor in Example 1-1.

Solution

The CE y parameters are

$$y_{ie} = (2 + j2) \times 10^{-3} \qquad y_{re} = (-2 - j20) \times 10^{-6}$$

$$y_{fe} = (20 - j3) \times 10^{-3} \qquad y_{oe} = (20 + j60) \times 10^{-6}$$

Observe that $g_{ie} > 0$ and $g_{oe} > 0$.

$$g_{ie} g_{oe} = (2 \times 10^{-3})(20 \times 10^{-6}) = 40 \times 10^{-9}$$

$$y_{re} y_{fe} = (-2 - j20)(20 - j3) \times 10^{-9}$$

$$= (-100 - j394) \times 10^{-9} = 406 \times 10^{-9} \; \underline{/256°}$$

Hence $P = -100 \times 10^{-9}$, and $M = \sqrt{P^2 + Q^2} = |y_{re} y_{fe}| = 406 \times 10^{-9}$

Substituting into the right side of (20) gives

$$\frac{P+\sqrt{P^2+Q^2}}{2}=\frac{-100\times10^{-9}+406\times10^{-9}}{2}=153\times10^{-9}$$

Since $g_{ie}g_{oe}<(P+\sqrt{P^2+Q^2})/2$, the transistor is potentially unstable in the CE configuration.

2-31 Linvill Stability Factor

The "degree" of stability given by inequality (23) is sometimes expressed by the Linvill stability factor C. Rearranging the inequality and recalling that $M\cos\theta=P$, this stability factor is defined to be

$$C=\frac{M}{2g_ig_o-P} \tag{24a}$$

It is sometimes found in the literature in the equivalent form

$$C=\frac{|y_r y_f|}{2\operatorname{Re}y_i\operatorname{Re}y_o-\operatorname{Re}(y_r y_f)} \tag{24b}$$

where Re denotes "real part of." When $1<C<\infty$ or when $C<0$, the transistor is potentially unstable, that is, oscillations can occur for certain selected passive terminations. When $0<C<1$, the transistor is inherently stable, that is, no passive terminations can cause oscillation without suitable external feedback. When $C=1$, the transistor is critically stable, that is, it is on the threshold of inherent stability and potential instability.

The Linvill stability factor can be expressed by the generalized k parameters as

$$C=\frac{|k_r k_f|}{2\operatorname{Re}k_i\operatorname{Re}k_o-|k_r k_f|\cos\theta} \tag{25}$$

where

$$\theta=\tan^{-1}\frac{\operatorname{Im}(k_r k_f)}{\operatorname{Re}(k_r k_f)} \tag{26}$$

If $\operatorname{Re}(k_i)>0$ and $\operatorname{Re}(k_o)>0$ and, furthermore, if $k_r=0$ (i.e., the device is unilateral), then $C=0$ and the transistor is inherently stable.

2-4 POWER GAINS

Several power gains are defined for the transistor circuit shown in Fig. 2-3.

1.   Operating power gain, defined as

$$G_p = \frac{P_{\text{out}}}{P_{\text{in}}} \tag{27}$$

where $P_{\text{out}} = |V_2|^2 G_L$ and $P_{\text{in}} = |V_1|^2 G_{\text{in}}$ are the actual operating powers delivered to the load by the transistor, and to the transistor by the signal source, respectively.

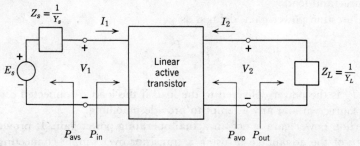

Figure 2-3. *Linear active transistor circuit.*

2.   Transducer power gain, defined as

$$G_T = \frac{P_{\text{out}}}{P_{\text{avs}}} \tag{28}$$

where P_{out} is the actual output power delivered to the load and P_{avs} is the available power from the source, that is,

$$P_{\text{avs}} = \frac{|E_s|^2}{4\,\text{Re}\,Z_s} \tag{29}$$

Transducer power gain is not an actual operating power gain unless the transistor is matched properly to the source. Transducer power gain provides a measure of the advantage of using a transistor over matching the same load to the source.

3. Available power gain, defined as

$$G_A = \frac{P_{\text{avo}}}{P_{\text{avs}}}$$

(30)

where P_{avo} is the available power from the transistor, that is,

$$P_{\text{avo}} = \frac{|E_{\text{th}}|^2}{4\,\text{Re}\,Z_{\text{th}}}$$

(31)

in which E_{th} and $Z_{\text{th}} = Z_{\text{out}}$ are the Thévenin equivalent voltage and impedance looking into the output port. Available power gain is not an actual operating power gain unless the transistor is properly matched to both the source and load.

4. Insertion power gain, defined as

$$G_I = \frac{P_{\text{out}}}{P_o'}$$

(32)

where P_o' is the power delivered to the load if the load is connected directly to the source without any attempt to provide matching.

Insertion power gain is not an actual operating power gain. It provides a measure of the advantage in using a transistor over simply connecting the same load directly to the source.

2-41 Operating Power Gain

Equation 27 becomes

$$G_p = \frac{|V_2|^2 G_L}{|V_1|^2 G_{\text{in}}} = |A_v|^2 \frac{G_L}{G_{\text{in}}}$$

(33)

The operating power gain is not particularly meaningful if G_{in} is either zero or negative, that is, if the transistor is potentially unstable. Assuming inherent stability, (33) becomes

$$G_p = \frac{|y_f|^2 G_L}{|y_o + Y_L|^2 \,\text{Re}\left(y_i - \frac{y_r y_f}{y_o + Y_L}\right)}$$

(34)

The optimum load admittance that maximizes G_p is found by setting the partial derivatives of G_p with respect to G_L and B_L equal to zero. This process is aided by letting

$$G_2 + jB_2 = y_o + Y_L = (g_o + G_L) + j(b_o + B_L) \tag{35}$$

$$y_r y_f = P + jQ = (g_r g_f - b_r b_f) + j(g_r b_f + g_f b_r) \tag{36}$$

Then (34) becomes

$$G_p = \frac{|y_f|^2 (G_2 - g_o)}{g_i (G_2^2 + B_2^2) - PG_2 - QB_2} \tag{37}$$

Forming $\partial G_p / \partial G_2 = 0$, solving the resulting quadratic for G_2, and using $G_2 = g_o + G_L$, yields the optimum load conductance given by

$$(G_L)_{opt} = \frac{1}{2g_i} \sqrt{(2g_i g_o - P)^2 - (P^2 + Q^2)} \tag{38}$$

Then forming $\partial G_p / \partial B_2 = 0$, solving for B_2, and using $B_2 = b_o + B_L$, yields the optimum load susceptance given by

$$(B_L)_{opt} = \frac{Q}{2g_i} - b_o \tag{39}$$

Equation 38 gives a real positive value for load conductance if

$$2g_i g_o - P > \sqrt{P^2 + Q^2} \tag{40}$$

This can be written as

$$g_i g_o > \frac{P + \sqrt{P^2 + Q^2}}{2} \tag{41}$$

which is exactly the same as one of the conditions for inherent stability given in (20).

The maximum operating power gain $(G_p)_{max}$ is found by substituting (38) and (39) into (37). This yields

$$(G_p)_{max} = \frac{|y_f|^2}{2g_i g_o - P + \sqrt{(2g_i g_o - P)^2 - (P^2 + Q^2)}} \tag{42}$$

$$= \frac{2|y_f|^2}{\left(\sqrt{2g_i g_o - P + \sqrt{P^2 + Q^2}} + \sqrt{2g_i g_o - P - \sqrt{P^2 + Q^2}} \right)^2} \tag{43}$$

The maximum operating power gain is real, finite, and positive for inherently stable transistor circuits. The optimum load necessary depends only on the transistor parameters and is independent of the source immittance. The input admittance is found to be, for the optimum load,

$$(G_{\text{in}})_{\text{opt}} = \frac{1}{2g_o}\sqrt{(2g_i g_o - P)^2 - (P^2 + Q^2)} \tag{44}$$

and

$$(B_{\text{in}})_{\text{opt}} = b_i - \frac{Q}{2g_o} \tag{45}$$

so

$$(Y_{\text{in}})_{\text{opt}} = (G_{\text{in}})_{\text{opt}} + j(B_{\text{in}})_{\text{opt}} \tag{46}$$

In order for the source to deliver maximum power to the transistor, the input admittance must be the conjugate of the source admittance $Y_s = G_s + jB_s$. Therefore, for maximum output power as well as maximum operating power gain,

$$(G_s)_{\text{opt}} = \frac{1}{2g_o}\sqrt{(2g_i g_o - P)^2 - (P^2 + Q^2)} \tag{47}$$

and

$$(B_s)_{\text{opt}} = \frac{Q}{2g_o} - b_i \tag{48}$$

so

$$(Y_s)_{\text{opt}} = (G_s)_{\text{opt}} + j(B_s)_{\text{opt}} \tag{49}$$

It is helpful to know the output admittance of the transistor when the source admittance is $(Y_s)_{\text{opt}}$. Symmetry of the expressions for input and output admittances allows the output admittance to be written by inspection of (44) and (45) after interchanging y_i and y_o, and interchanging Y_L and Y_s. Thus

$$(G_{\text{out}})_{\text{opt}} = \frac{1}{2g_i}\sqrt{(2g_i g_o - P)^2 - (P^2 + Q^2)} \tag{50}$$

and

$$(B_{\text{out}})_{\text{opt}} = b_o - \frac{Q}{2g_i} \tag{51}$$

so

$$(Y_{out})_{opt} = (G_{out})_{opt} + j(B_{out})_{opt} \qquad (52)$$

Comparing (50) and (51) with (38) and (39) indicates that there is a conjugate match between $(Y_{out})_{opt}$ and $(Y_L)_{opt}$. This means that the transistor delivers maximum power to the load.

2-411 Optimum Source Impedance. The source impedance required to maximize power delivered to the transistor must be determined with care. In Fig. 2-4b, if the voltage E_s is constant, and if Z_{in} is constant as determined by conditions for maximum power gain, then maximum power is delivered to the transistor when $R_s = 0$ and $X_s = -X_{in}$. The condition $R_s = 0$ imposes a difficult-to-achieve requirement directly on some signal sources, such as a previous amplifier stage or a matched transmission-line system where $R_s \neq 0$.

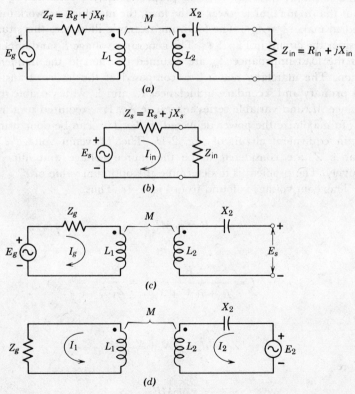

(a)

(b)

(c)

(d)

Figure 2-4. (a) *A matching network between the signal generator and load* Z_{in}. (b) *Thévenin equivalent of* (a). (c) *Circuit for finding* E_s. (d) *Circuit for finding* Z_s.

In such example cases, the voltage and impedance of the actual signal generator are usually fixed values. Then a passive impedance-matching network is inserted between the fixed generator and fixed load, and adjusted to allow maximum power to be delivered to the load. This means that the matching network must provide a conjugate match to the signal generator, which then delivers its available power. A conjugate match between the generator and matching network means that a conjugate match is also obtained between the load and the matching network. If the matching network is lossless, then the available power of the generator is delivered to the load.

When a matching network is used, the source impedance refers to that seen by the load looking back into the matching network, and is not equal to the actual generator impedance. In effect, this source impedance is the Thévenin series impedance Z_s, and the source voltage is the Thévenin voltage E_s. Here, the source voltage E_s is not constant but depends on the matching network; therefore it is not proper to use the condition $R_s = 0$. It turns out that to maximize power to the load, the matching network must be adjusted to make $Z_s = Z_{in}{}^*$. The following example illustrates this situation.

Consider the circuit in Fig. 2-4a. The generator voltage E_g and impedance Z_g and the load impedance Z_{in} are assumed constant at the frequency of operation. The matching network is composed of the lossless transformer having primary and secondary inductances L_1 and L_2 with variable mutual inductance M, and variable series reactance X_2. It is required to adjust M and X_2 to maximize the power delivered to Z_{in}. This can be done using the Thévenin equivalent circuit of Fig. 2-4b. The Thévenin voltage E_s and impedance Z_s are considered to be the source voltage and impedance, respectively. The problem is to determine the optimum value of Z_s.

The Thévenin voltage is found from Fig. 2-4c. Thus,

$$E_s = j\omega M I_g \tag{53}$$

But

$$I_g = \frac{E_g}{R_g + j(X_g + X_{L_1})} = \frac{E_g}{Z_{11}} \tag{54}$$

where

$$Z_{11} = R_g + j(X_g + X_{L_1})$$

Therefore,

$$E_s = \frac{j\omega M E_g}{Z_{11}} \tag{55}$$

and

$$|E_s|^2 = \frac{\omega^2 M^2 |E_g|^2}{|Z_{11}|^2} \tag{56}$$

Clearly E_s depends on the mutual inductance. Thus, as the coupling is changed to provide a match, E_s changes.

The Thévenin impedance is found from Fig. 2-4d to be

$$Z_s = \frac{E_2}{I_2} \tag{57}$$

Then

$$E_2 = j(X_{L_2} + X_2)I_2 - j\omega M I_1 \tag{58a}$$

$$0 = -j\omega M I_2 + I_1 Z_{11} \tag{58b}$$

Eliminating I_1 yields

$$Z_s = \frac{\omega^2 M^2 R_g}{|Z_{11}|^2} + j\left[X_{L_2} + X_2 - \frac{\omega^2 M^2 (X_g + X_{L_1})}{|Z_{11}|^2} \right] \tag{59}$$

Therefore,

$$R_s = \frac{\omega^2 M^2 R_g}{|Z_{11}|^2} \tag{60}$$

and

$$X_s = X_{L_2} + X_2 - \frac{\omega^2 M^2 (X_g + X_{L_1})}{|Z_{11}|^2} \tag{61}$$

The output power is found from Fig. 2-4b to be

$$P_o = |I_{in}|^2 R_{in} \tag{62}$$

The square of the current magnitude is

$$|I_{in}|^2 = \frac{|E_s|^2}{|Z_s + Z_{in}|^2}$$

$$= \frac{\omega^2 |E_g|^2}{|Z_{11}|^2} \frac{M^2}{\left(R_s + R_{in}\right)^2 + \left(X_s + X_{in}\right)^2} \tag{63}$$

Substituting for M^2 from (60) gives

$$|I_{in}|^2 = \frac{|E_g|^2}{R_g} \frac{R_s}{(R_s + R_{in})^2 + (X_s + X_{in})^2} \tag{64}$$

Since R_{in} is assumed constant, P_o is maximized when $|I_{in}|^2$ is maximized. This occurs when $X_{s,opt} = -X_{in}$ and $R_{s,opt} = R_{in}$ simultaneously. Therefore, maximum power output is obtained in this situation when $Z_{s,opt} = Z_{in}^*$, and its value is

$$(P_o)_{max} = \frac{|E_g|^2}{4R_g} \tag{65}$$

which equals the available power from the generator.

Finally, the optimum values of M and X_2 are found from (60) and (61). The optimum value of M makes $R_s = R_{in}$ and determines X_s in part. Then X_2 (which may be inductive or capacitive, depending on the numbers) is adjusted to make $X_s = -X_{in}$.

2-412 Condition for Simultaneous Conjugate Matching. For a conjugate match simultaneously at both ports,

$$Y_{in} = Y_s^* \tag{66}$$

and

$$Y_{out} = Y_L^* \tag{67}$$

In terms of the y parameters, the input and output admittances are

$$Y_{in} = \frac{D_y + y_i Y_L}{y_o + Y_L} = \frac{D_y + y_i Y_{out}^*}{y_o + Y_{out}^*} \tag{68}$$

and

$$Y_{out} = \frac{D_y + y_o Y_s}{y_i + Y_s} = \frac{D_y + y_o Y_{in}^*}{y_i + Y_{in}^*} \tag{69}$$

where $D_y = y_i y_o - y_r y_f$. From (69),

$$Y_{out}^* = \frac{D_y^* + y_o^* Y_{in}}{y_i^* + Y_{in}} \tag{70}$$

Substitute (70) into (68) and solve for Y_{in} to obtain

$$(y_o + y_o^*)Y_{in}^2 + (y_o y_i^* - y_o^* y_i + D_y^* - D_y)Y_{in} - y_i D_y^* - y_i^* D_y = 0 \tag{71}$$

This simplifies to

$$g_o Y_{in}^2 + \left[j(-2b_i g_o + b_r g_f + b_f g_r) \right] Y_{in} - (g_i \operatorname{Re} D_y + b_i \operatorname{Im} D_y) = 0 \quad (72)$$

where $y_i = g_i + jb_i$, $y_o = g_o + jb_o$, etc., and $D_y = \operatorname{Re} D_y + j\operatorname{Im} D_y$.

Equation 72 is a quadratic equation of the form $AY_{in}^2 + BY_{in} - C = 0$ in which the coefficients A and C are real, B is imaginary, and Y_{in} is complex. The usual quadratic formula applies, to yield

$$Y_{in} = -\frac{B}{2A} + \frac{1}{2A} \sqrt{B^2 + 4AC} \quad (73)$$

where $A = g_o$, $B = j(-2b_i g_o + b_r g_f + b_f g_r)$, and $C = g_i \operatorname{Re} D_y + b_i \operatorname{Im} D_y$.

Now $B/2A$ is always imaginary because of B, and B^2 is always negative, also because of B. Therefore, the $-B/2A$ term is considered to be the input susceptance jB_{in}, and the $\sqrt{B^2 + 4AC}/2A$ term is considered to be the input conductance G_{in}.

In order to achieve the conjugate match with a passive termination for which $G_s > 0$, the input conductance must be $G_{in} > 0$. So with $A = g_o > 0$, this means that $B^2 + 4AC > 0$, which also implies that $C > 0$.

After substituting for A, B, and C, and simplifying, it is recognized that

$$B^2 + 4AC = \left[2g_i g_o - \operatorname{Re}(y_r y_f) \right]^2 - |y_r y_f|^2 \quad (74)$$

Therefore the condition $B^2 + 4AC > 0$ for simultaneous conjugate match at both ports becomes

$$\left[2g_i g_o - \operatorname{Re}(y_r y_f) \right]^2 - |y_r y_f|^2 > 0 \quad (75)$$

which simplifies to

$$g_i g_o > \frac{\operatorname{Re}(y_r y_f) + |y_r y_f|}{2} \quad (76)$$

This is exactly the same as one of the conditions for inherent stability given in (20).

Because of the symmetry between (68) and (69), an expression for Y_{out} can be obtained from (73) by interchanging subscripts. Then $G_{out} > 0$ when condition (76) again is satisfied. Therefore, the condition for a conjugate match simultaneously at both ports is identical to one of the conditions for inherent stability.

The source and load terminations are readily determined. From (73) and (74),

$$G_s = G_{in} = \frac{\sqrt{B^2 + 4AC}}{2A} = \frac{1}{2g_o}\sqrt{\left[2g_i g_o - \text{Re}(y_r y_f)\right]^2 - |y_r y_f|^2} \quad (77)$$

which is the same as $(G_s)_{opt}$ from (47). Also, from (73),

$$jB_{in} = -\frac{B}{2A} = -j\frac{-2g_o b_i + b_r g_f + b_f g_r}{2g_o}$$

Thus

$$B_{in} = b_i - \frac{\text{Im}(y_r y_f)}{2g_o}$$

For the conjugate match,

$$B_s = -B_{in} = -b_i + \frac{\text{Im}(y_r y_f)}{2g_o} \quad (78)$$

which is the same as $(B_s)_{opt}$ from (48).

Interchanging subscripts yields

$$G_L = G_{out} = \frac{1}{2g_i}\sqrt{\left[2g_i g_o - \text{Re}(y_r y_f)\right]^2 - |y_r y_f|^2} \quad (79)$$

which is the same as $(G_L)_{opt}$ from (38).

$$B_L = -B_{out} = -b_o + \frac{\text{Im}(y_r y_f)}{2g_i} \quad (80)$$

which is the same as $(B_L)_{opt}$ from (39).

2-42 Transducer Power Gain

From (28), the transducer power gain is

$$G_T = \frac{4|y_f|^2 G_L G_s}{|(y_i + Y_s)(y_o + Y_L) - y_r y_f|^2} \quad (81)$$

To maximize G_T, consider first the effect of varying Y_L. It simplifies calculations considerably to rearrange (81) into a more convenient form.

Factor $|y_i + Y_s|^2$ from the denominator and use $Y_{out} - y_o = -y_r y_f / (y_i + Y_s)$ to obtain

$$G_T = \frac{4|y_f|^2 G_L G_s}{|y_i + Y_s|^2 |Y_L + Y_{out}|^2} \tag{82}$$

When B_L is changed, G_T is maximized with respect to B_L when $B_L = -B_{out}$. Then

$$(G_T)_{B_L} = \frac{4|y_f|^2 G_s G_L}{|y_i + Y_s|^2 (G_L + G_{out})^2} \tag{83}$$

Differentiating (83) with respect to G_L and equating to zero yields $G_L = G_{out}$. Therefore G_T is maximized with respect to Y_L when $Y_L = Y_{out}^*$, or a conjugate match exists at the output port. Then

$$(G_T)_{Y_L} = G_A = \frac{|y_f|^2 G_s}{G_L |y_i + Y_s|^2} \tag{84}$$

This is also the available power gain because the load is a conjugate match of the output immittance. The transistor delivers P_{avo} to the load.

Maximum transducer power gain is found by maximizing (84) with respect to Y_s. Of course, this also results in maximum available power gain. The procedure at this point is to set $\partial G_A / \partial G_s = 0$ and $\partial G_A / \partial B_s = 0$, and solve for the required values of G_s and B_s. It is helpful to let

$$G_1 + jB_1 = y_i + Y_s = (g_i + G_s) + j(b_i + B_s) \tag{85}$$

and

$$y_r y_f = P + jQ \tag{86}$$

Remembering that

$$G_L = G_{out} = \operatorname{Re}\left(y_o - \frac{y_r y_f}{y_i + Y_s}\right) \tag{87}$$

(84) becomes

$$G_A = \frac{|y_f|^2 (G_1 - g_i)}{g_o(G_1^2 + B_1^2) - PG_1 - QB_1} \tag{88}$$

Therefore $\partial G_A / \partial B_1 = 0$ yields

$$(B_1)_{\text{opt}} = \frac{Q}{2g_o} \tag{89}$$

or

$$(B_s)_{\text{opt}} = \frac{Q}{2g_o} - b_i \tag{90}$$

which is the same as (48).

Substituting (89) into (88) gives

$$(G_A)_{B_s} = \frac{|y_f|^2 (G_1 - g_i)}{g_o G_1^{\,2} - P G_1 - \dfrac{Q^2}{4g_o}} \tag{91}$$

Setting the partial derivative of (91) with respect to G_1 equal to zero, yields, after solving the resultant quadratic,

$$(G_1)_{\text{opt}} = g_i + \frac{1}{2g_o} \sqrt{(2g_i g_o - P)^2 - (P^2 + Q^2)} \tag{92}$$

so that

$$(G_s)_{\text{opt}} = (G_1)_{\text{opt}} - g_i = \frac{1}{2g_o} \sqrt{(2g_i g_o - P)^2 - (P^2 + Q^2)} \tag{93}$$

which is the same as (47).

Since the conditions for maximum transducer power gain and maximum available power gain are the same as for maximum operating power gain, then

$$(G_p)_{\text{max}} = (G_T)_{\text{max}} = (G_A)_{\text{max}} \tag{94}$$

2-43 Generalized Design Relationships

The optimum terminations and maximum power gains were derived in terms of the y parameters. Of course, either the z or h parameters could be used. In terms of the generalized parameters, the optimum terminations are

$$\text{Re}\,(\Gamma_L)_{\text{opt}} = \frac{1}{2\,\text{Re}\,k_i} \sqrt{\left[2\,\text{Re}\,k_i\,\text{Re}\,k_o - \text{Re}\,(k_r k_f)\right]^2 - |k_r k_f|^2} \tag{95}$$

$$\mathrm{Im}\,(\Gamma_L)_{\mathrm{opt}} = \frac{\mathrm{Im}\,(k_r k_f)}{2\,\mathrm{Re}\,k_i} - \mathrm{Im}\,k_o \qquad (96)$$

$$\mathrm{Re}\,(\Gamma_s)_{\mathrm{opt}} = \frac{1}{2\,\mathrm{Re}\,k_o} \sqrt{\left[2\,\mathrm{Re}\,k_i\,\mathrm{Re}\,k_o - \mathrm{Re}\,(k_r k_f)\right]^2 - |k_r k_f|^2} \qquad (97)$$

$$\mathrm{Im}\,(\Gamma_s)_{\mathrm{opt}} = \frac{\mathrm{Im}\,(k_r k_f)}{2\,\mathrm{Re}\,k_o} - \mathrm{Im}\,k_i \qquad (98)$$

The maximum operating power gain is

$$(G_p)_{\mathrm{max}} = \frac{|k_f|^2}{2\,\mathrm{Re}\,k_i\,\mathrm{Re}\,k_o - \mathrm{Re}\,(k_r k_f) + \sqrt{\left[2\,\mathrm{Re}\,k_i\,\mathrm{Re}\,k_o - \mathrm{Re}\,(k_r k_f)\right]^2 - |k_r k_f|^2}}$$

$$(99)$$

$$= \frac{|k_f|^2}{\left[\sqrt{2\,\mathrm{Re}\,k_i\,\mathrm{Re}\,k_o - \mathrm{Re}\,(k_r k_f) + |k_r k_f|} + \sqrt{2\,\mathrm{Re}\,k_i\,\mathrm{Re}\,k_o - \mathrm{Re}\,(k_r k_f) - |k_r k_f|}\,\right]^2}$$

$$(100)$$

Example   2-2

The CE y parameters of a 2N3783 transistor at 200 MHz are

$$y_{ie} = (20 + j13) \times 10^{-3} \qquad y_{re} = (-0.015 - j0.502) \times 10^{-3}$$

$$y_{fe} = (41.5 - j64) \times 10^{-3} \qquad y_{oe} = (0.25 + j1.9) \times 10^{-3}$$

Determine the optimum terminations and maximum power gain.

Solution

First, establish whether or not the transistor is inherently stable by using (24).

$$y_r y_f = 38.3 \times 10^{-6} \; \underline{/211.3} = (-32.7 - j19.94) \times 10^{-6}$$

$$C = \frac{38.3 \times 10^{-6}}{2(20 \times 10^{-3})(0.25 \times 10^{-3}) - (-32.7 \times 10^{-6})} = 0.895$$

Therefore inherent stability is established.

The optimum terminations are found from (95) through (98). Hence

$$\text{Re}(Y_L)_{\text{opt}} = 0.47 \times 10^{-3}$$

$$\text{Im}(Y_L)_{\text{opt}} = -2.4 \times 10^{-3}$$

$$\text{Re}(Y_s)_{\text{opt}} = 37.6 \times 10^{-3}$$

$$\text{Im}(Y_s)_{\text{opt}} = -53 \times 10^{-3}$$

The maximum power gain is found from (99). Thus $(G_p)_{\text{max}} = 94.1 = 19.73$ dB.

2-5 UNILATERAL POWER GAIN

A transistor whose generalized reverse transmission parameter k_r is zero, or sufficiently small to be regarded as zero, is said to be unilateral. From (1-41)

$$U = \frac{|k_f|^2}{4 \, \text{Re} \, k_i \, \text{Re} \, k_o} \tag{101}$$

Again, if $U > 1$, the transistor is active.

From (25), the Linvill stability factor is $C = 0$, so the unilateral transistor is inherently stable provided $\text{Re} \, k_i > 0$ and $\text{Re} \, k_o > 0$.

The maximum operating power gain is

$$(G_p)_u = \frac{|k_f|^2}{4 \, \text{Re} \, k_i \, \text{Re} \, k_o} \tag{102}$$

and is known as the unilateral power gain. Notice that $U = (G_p)_u$ for the unilateral transistor.

The optimum terminations are

$$\text{Re}(\Gamma_L)_{\text{opt}} = \text{Re} \, k_o \tag{103}$$

$$\text{Im}(\Gamma_L)_{\text{opt}} = -\text{Im} \, k_o \tag{104}$$

$$\text{Re}(\Gamma_s)_{\text{opt}} = \text{Re} \, k_i \tag{105}$$

$$\text{Im}(\Gamma_s)_{\text{opt}} = -\text{Im} \, k_i \tag{106}$$

These terminations provide a conjugate match at each port and they are completely decoupled.

2-6 TUNABILITY

The optimum terminations for a transistor amplifier are usually obtained in practice by adjusting the values of the components in the matching networks. Ease of tunability, or alignability, depends on the fractional change in input immittance compared to the fractional change in load immittance, and on the fractional change in output immittance compared to the fractional change in source immittance. When the fractional changes in input and output immittances are small, it is not necessary to alternate many times between input and output tuning to achieve the desired condition of operation.

In terms of the y parameters, the input admittance is

$$Y_{in} = y_i - \frac{y_r\, y_f}{y_o + Y_L} \tag{107}$$

Then

$$\frac{dY_{in}}{dY_L} = \frac{y_r\, y_f}{(y_o + Y_L)^2} \tag{108}$$

The fractional change in input admittance is dY_{in}/Y_{in} and the fractional change in load admittance is dY_L/Y_L. Therefore, dividing (108) by

$$\frac{Y_{in}}{Y_L} = \frac{y_i}{Y_L} - \frac{y_f\, y_f}{Y_L(y_o + Y_L)} \tag{109}$$

gives the input tunability or alignability factor that is defined to be

$$\delta = \frac{|dY_{in}/Y_{in}|}{|dY_L/Y_L|} = \frac{|y_r\, y_f|\ |Y_L|}{|y_o + Y_L|\ |y_i(y_o + Y_L) - y_r\, y_f|} \tag{110}$$

Tuning is easier as δ is made smaller. From (110), $\delta = 0$ when $Y_L = 0$ or when $Y_L \to \infty$, but such extreme admittances do not allow much power gain. Also, $\delta = 0$ when $y_f = 0$, but then there is no power gain. Making $y_r = 0$ for $\delta = 0$ is a consequence of unilateralization and the output circuit has no effect whatsoever on the input circuit.

In order to achieve good tunability in a well-designed tuned amplifier, the load admittance may be chosen such that $Y_L \gg y_o$ in order to make $\delta < 0.3$. Then (110) becomes

$$\delta \cong \frac{|y_r\, y_f|}{|y_i|\ |Y_L|} \tag{111}$$

For Example 2-2, the tunability factor is, from (110)

$$\delta \cong \frac{(38.3 \times 10^{-6})(2.44 \times 10^{-3})}{(0.876 \times 10^{-3})(57.0 \times 10^{-6})} = 1.87$$

Since δ is rather large, the amplifier would be somewhat difficult to tune. By redesigning the amplifier to make $\delta \leqslant 0.3$, a larger load admittance is necessary than that which gives maximum power gain. Therefore mismatching improves tunability.

If $\delta = 0.3$, then (111) gives for the load admittance

$$|Y_L| \cong \frac{|y_r y_f|}{|y_i| (0.3)} \tag{112a}$$

Then, by assuming

$$|Y_L| \cong G_L \tag{112b}$$

the value of B_L is found that maximizes the power gain for fixed G_L. This procedure is outlined in Chapter 5.

2-7 BANDWIDTHS

The output power varies with frequency partly because the transistor parameters are frequency dependent but primarily because the conditions for a conjugate match at the input and output ports may not be obtained except at the design-center frequency f_0. At either port, conjugate matching means that two parallel conductances of equal value are in parallel with capacitive and inductive susceptances of equal value at the center frequency.

The amplifier bandwidth can be approximated under certain conditions from the inherent bandwidth $(BW)^i$ at either port given by

$$(BW)^i_{\text{out}} = \frac{2f_0 (G_L)_{\text{opt}}}{|(B_L)_{\text{opt}}|} \text{ Hz} \tag{113}$$

for the output circuit, and by

$$(BW)^i_{\text{in}} = \frac{2f_0 (G_s)_{\text{opt}}}{|(B_s)_{\text{opt}}|} \text{ Hz} \tag{114}$$

for the input circuit. Inherent bandwidth is the name given to the bandwidth that is obtained in the conjugate matching situation where the optimum terminations are determined only by the transistor parameters.

Therefore, the circuit designer is not free to arbitrarily specify the inherent bandwidth of either port after the transistor has been selected.

Substituting the optimum terminations from Section 2-43 into (113) and (114) gives

$$\frac{(BW)^i_{\text{in}}}{(BW)^i_{\text{out}}} = \frac{Q - 2g_i b_o}{Q - 2g_o b_i} \tag{115}$$

It often happens that the inherent bandwidth of the input circuit is appreciably larger than that of the output circuit. In such cases, the overall amplifier bandwidth and selectivity are determined primarily by the output circuit.

Equations (113) and (114) indicate that the bandwidths are inversely proportional to the optimum terminating susceptances. Equations 96 and 98 show that the optimum terminating susceptances can be increased by adding capacitive susceptances across the input and output terminals where they act as part of $\text{Im}\, y_i$ and $\text{Im}\, y_o$, respectively. Therefore, the bandwidth of the input or output can be decreased below the inherent bandwidth by adding shunt capacitances C_L or C_s across the output and input terminals, respectively. The bandwidths become

$$BW_{\text{out}} = \frac{2f_0 (G_L)_{\text{opt}}}{|(B_L)_{\text{opt}}| + \omega_0 C_L} \tag{116}$$

and

$$BW_{\text{in}} = \frac{2f_0 (G_s)_{\text{opt}}}{|(B_s)_{\text{opt}}| + \omega_0 C_s} \tag{117}$$

Solving (116) and (117) for the additional shunt capacitances yields

$$C_L = \frac{1}{2\pi} \left[\frac{2(G_L)_{\text{opt}}}{BW_{\text{out}}} - \frac{|(B_L)_{\text{opt}}|}{f_0} \right] \tag{118}$$

and

$$C_s = \frac{1}{2\pi} \left[\frac{2(G_s)_{\text{opt}}}{BW_{\text{in}}} - \frac{|(B_s)_{\text{opt}}|}{f_0} \right] \tag{119}$$

When C_L and C_s are used to decrease the bandwidths, the required load and source susceptances become

$$-jB_L = -j\left[(B_L)_{\text{opt}} + \omega_0 C_L \right] \tag{120}$$

and

$$-jB_s = -j\left[(B_s)_{\text{opt}} + \omega_0 C_s\right] \tag{121}$$

Narrow-banding the amplifier by adding shunt capacitances C_L and C_s does not affect the optimum terminating conductances because (95) and (97) are independent of $\text{Im} y_o$ and $\text{Im} y_i$. Maximum operating power gain is still obtained as the bandwidth is decreased by adding shunt capacitances.

When an inherent bandwidth is too small for a particular application, (113) and (114) indicate that the bandwidth can be increased by raising the optimum terminating conductance. This means that additional shunt resistance can be connected across the input or output terminals. The power gain is decreased when the bandwidth is increased by adding shunt resistance.

If the bandwidths of the input and output circuits are made equal, the overall bandwidth is

$$BW_{\text{overall}} = BW_{\text{circuit}} \sqrt{2^{1/2} - 1} = 0.644\, BW_{\text{circuit}} \tag{122}$$

In general, for single-tuned circuits,

$$BW_{\text{overall}} = BW_{\text{circuit}} \sqrt{2^{1/n} - 1} \tag{123}$$

where n is the number of identical-bandwidth circuits.

Example 2-3

For the amplifier in Example 2-2, determine the additional shunt capacitances for an overall bandwidth of 2 MHz assuming the bandwidths of the input and output circuits are made equal.

Solution

The inherent bandwidths are

$$(BW)^i_{\text{out}} = \frac{2(200 \times 10^6)(0.47 \times 10^{-3})}{2.4 \times 10^{-3}} = 78.4 \text{ MHz}$$

$$(BW)^i_{\text{in}} = \frac{2(200 \times 10^6)(37.6 \times 10^{-3})}{53 \times 10^{-3}} = 284 \text{ MHz}$$

Actually, in practice, such broad bandwidths cannot be obtained because of variations of the transistor parameters with frequency.

From (122), the bandwidth of each circuit at the input and output ports is

$$BW_{\text{circuit}} = \frac{BW_{\text{overall}}}{\sqrt{2^{1/2} - 1}} = \frac{2 \text{ MHz}}{0.644} = 3.11 \text{ MHz}$$

Substituting into (118) and (119) yields

$$C_L = \frac{1}{2\pi} \left[\frac{2(0.47 \times 10^{-3})}{3.11 \times 10^6} - \frac{2.4 \times 10^{-3}}{200 \times 10^6} \right] \cong 46 \text{ pF}$$

and

$$C_s = \frac{1}{2\pi} \left[\frac{2(37.6 \times 10^{-3})}{3.11 \times 10^6} - \frac{53 \times 10^{-3}}{200 \times 10^6} \right] \cong 0.0038 \mu\text{F}$$

The required load and source susceptances are

$$B_L = (B_L)_{\text{opt}} + \omega_0 C_L = 2.4 \times 10^{-3} + 2\pi (200 \times 10^6)(46 \times 10^{-12})$$

$$= 60.4 \times 10^{-3} \text{ mho}$$

$$B_s = (B_s)_{\text{opt}} + \omega_0 C_s = 53 \times 10^{-3} + 2\pi (200 \times 10^6)(3.8 \times 10^{-9})$$

$$= 4.83 \text{ mhos}$$

If no effort is made to narrow the inherent bandwidth of the input circuit, the overall bandwidth of the amplifier is effectively produced by the output circuit with the additional shunt capacitance

$$C_L = \frac{1}{2\pi} \left[\frac{2(0.47 \times 10^{-3})}{2 \times 10^6} - \frac{2.4 \times 10^{-3}}{200 \times 10^6} \right] \cong 73 \text{ pF}$$

PROBLEMS

2-1. For each of the following CE parameter sets, determine if the transistor is potentially unstable or inherently stable.

(a)	(b)	(c)
$y_{ie} = (20 + j10)10^{-3}$	$y_{ie} = (2 + j2)10^{-3}$	$h_{ie} = 1500$
$y_{re} = (-1 - j0.5)10^{-3}$	$y_{re} = (-2 - j20)10^{-6}$	$h_{re} = 3 \times 10^{-4}$
$y_{fe} = (40 - j100)10^{-3}$	$y_{fe} = (20 - j3)10^{-3}$	$h_{fe} = 40$
$y_{oe} = (1 + j5)10^{-3}$	$y_{oe} = (20 + j60)10^{-6}$	$h_{oe} = 3 \times 10^{-5}$

2-2. Determine if the transistors whose CE parameters are given in Problem 2-1 are potentially unstable when used as emitter followers.

2-3. The CE parameters of a transistor at 60 MHz are

$$y_{ie} = (6.8 + j6.1)10^{-3} \qquad y_{re} = (-j0.81)10^{-3}$$

$$y_{fe} = (33.6 - j44.2)10^{-3} \qquad y_{oe} = (1.24 + j1.92)10^{-3}$$

Determine:

(*a*) If the transistor is inherently stable.

(*b*) The optimum load and source terminations.

(*c*) The maximum operating power gain in decibels.

(*d*) Inherent bandwidths.

(*e*) Additional capacitances C_L and C_s to make the bandwidth of the input and output circuits each 2 MHz.

(*f*) Overall bandwidth for (*e*).

(*g*) Optimum terminations for (*e*).

(*h*) Operating power gain in decibels for (*g*). Compare with result of (*c*).

(*i*) Calculate tunability factors for (*b*) and (*g*).

2-4.   A two-port network is shown in Fig. 2.5.

(*a*) Is the network potentially unstable?

(*b*) If $n < 1$, what range of values for n makes it possible for R_{in} and R_{out} to become negative?

(*c*) If $n = 1.5$, what ranges of positive real values for R_L and R_S make the entire network stable?

(*d*) If $0 < n < 1$, what ranges of positive real values for R_L and R_S make the entire network stable?

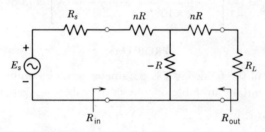

Figure 2-5.   Circuit for Problem 2-4.

2-5.   The CE parameters of a transistor at 50 MHz are

$$y_{ie} = (2 + j0.25)10^{-3} \qquad y_{re} = (-j0.15)10^{-3}$$
$$y_{fe} = (50 - j20)10^{-3} \qquad y_{oe} = (0.05 + j0.4)10^{-3}$$

(*a*) Is the transistor potentially unstable?

(*b*) Specify simple load and source terminations for which the circuit is unstable.

(*c*) Repeat (*b*) for a stable circuit.

CHAPTER THREE

CIRCUIT DESIGN AIDS

3-0 INTRODUCTION

Numerous aids are available to the circuit designer in the forms of charts, graphs, monographs, and tables of calculated values. One of the most useful of all design aids is the Smith chart. Not only is the Smith chart useful in transmission line, waveguide, and antenna problems, but it is one of the best ways to present parameter variations with frequency. Circuit design in terms of scattering parameters is best performed with the help of a Smith chart, as well as the design of potentially unstable circuits. Matching networks generally required to provide optimum terminations or terminations for other conditions are quickly designed using the Smith chart. In addition, the Smith chart can be used to provide a good, general, overall view of the scope of a particular situation.

Although microstrip is more of a basic circuit component than a design aid, data is also presented on microstrip and its uses. High-frequency amplifiers sometimes can use short lengths of microstrip as tuning stubs, matching networks, isolators, and interconnections. Calculations pertaining to microstrip generally involve the Smith chart.

3-1 THE SMITH CHART*

Basically the Smith chart is a transformation between an impedance Z and the reflection coefficient $R \underline{/\phi}$, of a transmission line, which has the form

$$R \underline{/\phi} = \frac{Z - Z_o}{Z + Z_o} \qquad (1)$$

*Modernized Smith charts and accessories are commercially available from Analog Instruments Company, New Providence, NJ, 07974.

55

where Z_o represents the characteristic impedance of the line or a reference impedance whose value depends on how the Smith chart is to be used.

Let

$$\frac{Z}{Z_o} = z = r + jx \tag{2}$$

and

$$R \underline{/\phi} = U + jV \tag{3}$$

Then (1) becomes

$$U + jV = \frac{r - 1 + jx}{r + 1 + jx} \tag{4}$$

Solving for the real and imaginary parts gives

$$U = \frac{r^2 - 1 + x^2}{(r+1)^2 + x^2} \quad \text{and} \quad V = \frac{2x}{(r+1)^2 + x^2} \tag{5}$$

Eliminate x to obtain

$$\left(U - \frac{r}{r+1}\right)^2 + V^2 = \left(\frac{1}{r+1}\right)^2 \tag{6}$$

which is the equation for a family of circles whose centers are at $U = r/(r+1)$, $V = 0$, and whose radii are $1/(r+1)$. Several circles are shown in Fig. 3-1a for only positive values of r because negative values are not encountered in passive circuits.

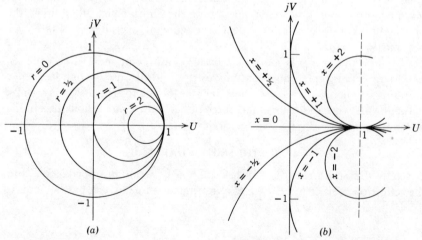

Figure 3-1.   Smith chart construction: (a) r circles; (b) x circles.

Eliminate r from (5) to obtain

$$(U-1)^2 + \left(V - \frac{1}{x}\right)^2 = \left(\frac{1}{x}\right)^2 \tag{7}$$

which represents a family of circles with centers at $U = 1$, $V = 1/x$, and radii $1/x$. Several circles are shown in Fig. 3-1b for both positive and negative values of x.

When the two sets of circles are combined to form a Smith chart, the U and V axes are discarded, a linear scale for R provided, and positive and negative angles ϕ marked around the outside of the $r = 0$ circle. Additional radially scaled parameters pertaining to loss and standing-wave ratio, and wavelength scales around the outside circumference, are also available for transmission-line problems. A Smith chart is shown in Fig. 3-1c.

The same set of r circles is used to represent the conductance component of admittance Y divided by reference admittance Y_o. Numerical values for these normalized resistance or conductance components are marked along the discarded U axis. The x circles above the horizontal axis represent the normalized inductive reactance components or the normalized capacitive susceptance components. Below the horizontal axis, the x circles represent normalized capacitance reactance components or normalized inductive susceptance components.

The usual tools for working with a Smith chart are a straightedge, a compass, and a slide rule or a small electronic calculator. Good accuracy can be obtained with unhurried and careful graphical constructions.

Example 3-1

A lossless transmission line whose characteristic impedance is $50 + j0$ Ω is terminated in a load impedance of $50 + j100$ Ω. Determine the reflection coefficient and standing-wave ratio.

Solution

The normalized components are $z = (50 + j100)/50 = 1 + j2$. Locate the intersection of the $r = 1$ and $x = +2$ circles. Lay the straightedge through the intersection and center of the Smith chart. Read $+45$ degrees where the straightedge crosses the angle-of-reflection-coefficient scale. Using the compass as dividers, transfer the radial distance between the Smith chart center and the point of intersection to the linear voltage-reflection-coefficient scale and read 0.707. Therefore the reflection coefficient is $0.707 \; \underline{/+45°}$. When the same radial distance is transferred to the standing-wave ratio scale, the voltage standing-wave ratio is found to be about 6.0. The voltage standing-wave ratio scale is the same as the r-circle markings from 1 to ∞, so that a

IMPEDANCE OR ADMITTANCE COORDINATES

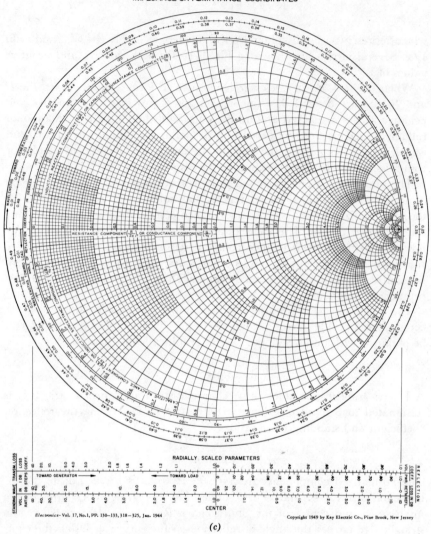

RADIALLY SCALED PARAMETERS

Electronics- Vol. 17, No.1, PP. 130–133, 318–325, Jan. 1944

(c)

Figure 3-1.   (c) The Smith chart.   Copyrighted by and reproduced with the permission of Kay Electric Company, Pine Brook, N.J.

separate scale for VSWR is not actually needed. The construction is shown in Fig. 3.2.

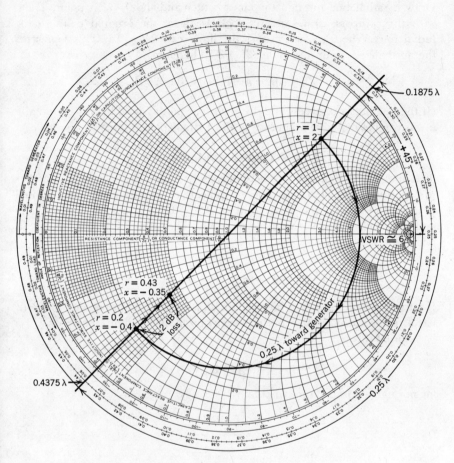

Figure 3-2. Smith chart construction for Examples 3-1 and 3-2.

Example 3-2

The lossless line of Example 3-1 is one-quarter wavelength long. Determine the input impedance.

Solution

The straightedge through the chart center and the intersection point passes through 0.1875 on the wavelengths-toward-generator outside scale, as shown in Fig. 3-2. This scale is used because it is necessary to move 0.25λ from the load toward the generator to find input impedance. Therefore, add 0.25λ and 0.1875λ to obtain 0.4375λ, which corresponds to the input terminals. Draw a radial line through the chart center and the 0.4375λ point. Then, with the compass, draw an arc clockwise from the original point to the radial line. Where the arc crosses the line, read $0.2 - j0.4$. This represents the normalized input impedance Z_{in}/Z_o. Therefore

$$Z_{in} = (0.2 - j0.4)(50) = 10 - j20 \ \Omega$$

(If the line had a total loss of 2 dB, the input point would be moved radially inward to $0.43 - j0.35$, according to the 1-dB-steps transmission loss scale.)

3-11 Reciprocals of Immittances

The numbers in Example 3-2 were purposely chosen also to indicate another use of the Smith chart: finding reciprocals of immittances. The original point at $1 + j2$ and the final point at $0.2 - j0.4$ are located diametrically opposite each other at equal chart radius. The values are also reciprocals because

$$\frac{1}{1 + j2} = \frac{1 - j2}{1^2 + 2^2} = \frac{1}{5} - j\frac{2}{5} = 0.2 - j0.4$$

If a transmission line is not involved at all, a normalized impedance of $1 + j2$ has a reciprocal $0.2 - j0.4$ that represents normalized admittance.

As proof solve

$$R \underline{/\phi} = \frac{z - 1}{z + 1} \tag{8}$$

for normalized impedance to obtain

$$z = \frac{1 + R \underline{/\phi}}{1 - R \underline{/\phi}} \tag{9}$$

The reciprocal of (9) becomes the normalized admittance

$$y = \frac{1 - R \underline{/\phi}}{1 + R \underline{/\phi}} \tag{10}$$

Suppose the value of ϕ in (9) is changed by $\pm 180°$. On the Smith chart, this corresponds to points diametrically opposite to z. Then, the right side of (9) becomes

$$\frac{1 + R \underline{/\phi \pm 180°}}{1 - R \underline{/\phi \pm 180°}} \tag{11}$$

When $\pm 180°$ is added to the angle of a complex number, the result is the same as taking the negative of the original number. Thus (11) becomes

$$\frac{1 - R \,\underline{/\phi}}{1 + R \,\underline{/\phi}} \tag{12}$$

which is the reciprocal of (9). Reciprocals are illustrated in Fig. 3-3.

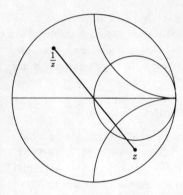

Figure 3-3. *Reciprocals anywhere on a Smith chart are diametrically opposite at equal radius.*

3-12 Negative resistances

Special problem cases sometimes arise that require careful handling. These generally involve negative resistances or reflection coefficients greater than unity, and occur when the difference between the angles of Z and Z_o is greater than 90°. For example, if $Z = j5$ and $Z_o = 3 - j4$, then $z = -0.8 + j0.6$ and $R = j3 = 3 \,\underline{/90°}$. Neither $r = -0.8$ nor $R = 3 \,\underline{/90°}$ can be located inside the usual Smith chart. For all such cases

$$R \,\underline{/\phi} = \frac{-r - 1 + jx}{-r + 1 + jx} \tag{13}$$

Consider the conjugate of the reciprocal of (13). Thus

$$\frac{1}{R \,\underline{/-\phi}} = \left(\frac{-r + 1 + jx}{-r - 1 + jx} \right)^* = \frac{-r + 1 - jx}{-r - 1 - jx} \tag{14}$$

Now let

$$\frac{1}{R \,\underline{/-\phi}} = U + jV \tag{15}$$

Then, from (14),

$$U = \frac{r^2 - 1 + x^2}{(r+1)^2 + x^2} \quad \text{and} \quad V = \frac{2x}{(r+1)^2 + x^2} \tag{16}$$

which are the same as the two previous relationships for the Smith chart. Thus, if $|R| > 1$, locate $1/R^*$ and interpret the resistance circles as being negative and the reactance circles as marked. For $R = 3 \; \underline{/90°}$, $1/R^* = 0.33 \; \underline{/90°}$, for which $z = -0.8 + j0.6$.

The presence of negative resistance does not change the reciprocal relationships discussed in Section 3-11. If the original point has negative resistance, its reciprocal has a negative real component also. For example, $z = -0.8 + j0.6$ has a reciprocal located diametrically opposite at equal radius, and is located at $-0.8 - j0.6$.

3-2 IMMITTANCE MATCHING

A useful application of the Smith chart is in the design of matching networks. Many high-frequency amplifiers deliver power to a properly terminated 50-Ω transmission line. However, if the amplifiers operate under conditions of maximum power gain, the optimum terminations are different from 50-Ω resistance. Therefore, lossless networks are desirable to change the 50 Ω of transmission line load resistance into the desired optimum terminations.

Many different combinations of lumped elements and sections of transmission lines are possible to effect matching. The simplest lumped matching networks are the ell sections shown in Fig. 3-4. Which type must be used depends on the value of $(Z_L)_{opt} = 1/(Y_L)_{opt}$ [or $(Z_s)_{opt} = 1/(Y_s)_{opt}$]. Four other ell networks employ either two capacitors or two inductances.

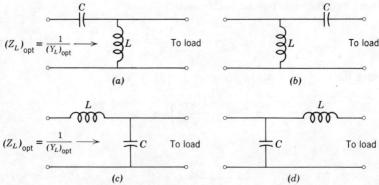

Figure 3-4.   Ell-section matching networks.

Consider first the circuit in Fig. 3-4a. Inductive susceptance is in parallel with the line load susceptance. Assuming the load to be a transmission line terminated in Z_o (resistive at high frequencies), use Z_o as the normalizing impedance. Then the normalized line load is $z_o = 1 + j0$, so that adding the normalized inductive susceptance in parallel gives normalized parallel admittance $y_{AB} = 1 - jb_{AB}$. The locus of points for y_{AB} is the bottom half of the conductance component circle for $G/Y_o = 1$ as shown in Fig. 3-5a. The locus of the reciprocals of y_{AB} also is a semicircle as shown. It has the same radius as the $G/Y_o = 1$ circle and, in matching-network design using this circuit, it should be drawn on the Smith chart. Since capacitive reactance is added to z_{AB}, the Smith chart is now considered to be in terms of impedance instead of the previously used admittances. As normalized capacitive reactance is added, the locus of points for $(z_L)_{opt}$ moves in a counterclockwise manner along a constant r circle an amount depending on C and frequency. All points in the non-crosshatched region of the Smith chart represent values of $(z_L)_{opt}$ that can be obtained with this circuit. The crosshatched region represents the reciprocals of $(z_L)_{opt}$ points and is the location of all $(y_L)_{opt}$ that can be obtained with this circuit.

The design procedure using this circuit is as follows. Calculate $(y_L)_{opt}$ and verify that it falls in the crosshatched region of Fig. 3-5a, say at point 1. Construct the reciprocal of $(y_L)_{opt}$ and locate point 2. Of course, if $(z_L)_{opt}$ is calculated or otherwise known, point 2 is established immediately. Note the values of the r and x circles passing through point 2. Draw the semicircle representing the locus of z_{AB}. Observe that it crosses the same r circle at point 3. Note the value of the x circle passing through point 3. Then the series capacitive reactance of C is given by

$$X_C = \frac{1}{\omega C} = Z_o(x_3 - x_2) \qquad (17)$$

where x_3 and x_2 are the values of the x circles (algebraic signs included) passing through points 3 and 2, respectively. Next construct the reciprocal of point 3 to obtain point 4, which must fall on the $G/Y_o = 1$ circle. Note the magnitude of the susceptance circle passing through point 4. The inductive susceptance of L is given by

$$B = -\frac{1}{\omega L} = Y_o(-b_4) = \frac{-b_4}{Z_o} \qquad (18)$$

Therefore, the inductive reactance of L is

$$X_L = \omega L = \frac{Z_o}{b_4} \qquad (19)$$

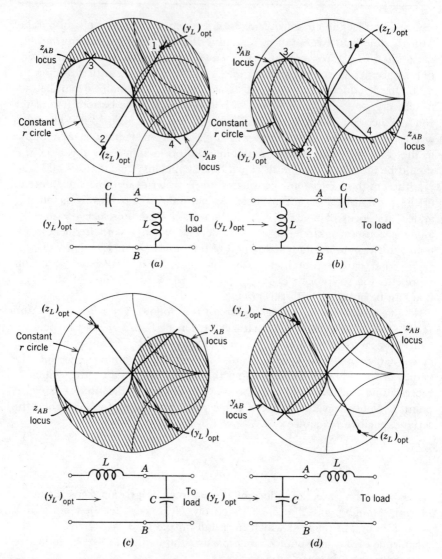

Figure 3-5. Smith chart constructions for transforming load immittances to optimum transistor terminations. The crosshatched regions represent locations of transformable terminations for the circuits shown.

where b_4 is the magnitude of the susceptance circle passing through point 4. Knowing Z_o and frequency, the values of L and C can be determined.

Consider next the circuit of Fig. 3-4b. Here, capacitive reactance is added to the line load resistance causing the locus of z_{AB} to be along the $r = 1$ circle as shown in Fig. 3-5b. The reciprocal of these points gives again the semicircle, which now represents the locus of y_{AB}. Adding the inductive susceptance of the parallel L causes the acceptable values of $(y_L)_{opt}$ to be as shown in the crosshatched region of Fig. 3-5b.

The design procedure using this circuit is as follows: Calculate $(y_L)_{opt}$ and verify that it falls in the proper crosshatched region, say at point 2 in Fig. 3-5b. Of course, if $(z_L)_{opt}$ is known at point 1, its reciprocal gives point 2. Note the values of the g and b circles passing through point 2. Draw the semicircle representing the locus of y_{AB}. Observe that it crosses the same g circle at point 3. Note the value of the b circle passing through point 3. The parallel inductive susceptance of L is given by

$$B = \frac{1}{\omega L} = Y_o(b_3 - b_2) = \frac{b_3 - b_2}{Z_o} \tag{20}$$

or the inductive reactance is

$$\omega L = \frac{Z_o}{b_3 - b_2} \tag{21}$$

where b_3 and b_2 are the values of the b circles (algebraic signs included) passing through points 3 and 2, respectively. Next, construct the reciprocal of point 3 to obtain point 4, which must fall on the $R/Z_o = 1$ circle. Note the magnitude of the reactance circle passing through point 4. The capacitive reactance of C is

$$X_C = -\frac{1}{\omega C} = Z_o(-x_4) \tag{22}$$

where x_4 is the magnitude of the reactance circle passing through point 4. Knowing Z_o and frequency, the values of L and C for this circuit can be determined.

The validity and design procedures for the Smith chart constructions and circuits given in Fig. 3-5c and d are left as exercises for the students.

Example 3-3

Design the input and output matching networks for the amplifier in Example 2-2 when inserted into a 50-Ω transmission line.

Solution

$$(y_L)_{\text{opt}} = \frac{(0.47 - j2.4) \times 10^{-3}}{1/50} = 0.0235 - j0.12$$

This point is located in the transformable region of Fig. 3-5b. The susceptance circle passing through this point is -0.12 as shown in Fig. 3-6a. The susceptance at point 3, the intersection of the arc and $g = 0.0235$ circle, is found to be $+0.156$. Therefore, the value of L, from (21), is

$$L = \frac{50}{2\pi(200 \times 10^6)(0.156 + 0.12)} = 0.144 \ \mu\text{H}$$

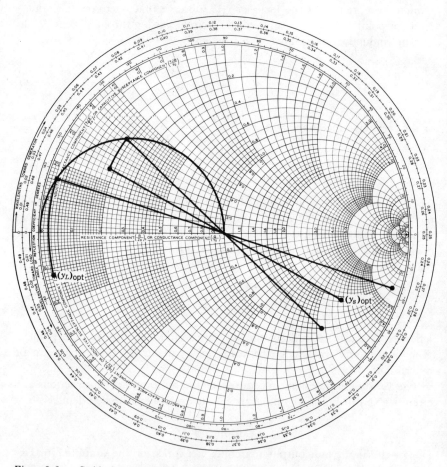

Figure 3-6a.   Smith chart construction for Example 3-3.

The reciprocal of point 3 is at $1 - j6.6$ (at point 4). Hence the capacitive reactance magnitude is 6.6. From (22), the capacitance is

$$C = \frac{1}{2\pi(200 \times 10^6)(50)(6.6)} = 2.41 \text{ pF}$$

For the input circuit,

$$(y_s)_{\text{opt}} = \frac{(37.6 - j53) \times 10^{-3}}{1/50} = 1.88 - j2.65$$

This point falls in the transformable region of Fig. 3-5a. Its reciprocal is point 2 at $0.18 + j0.25$. The semicircle crosses the $r = 0.18$ circle at $+ j0.385$ (point 3). From (17), the capacitance is

$$C = \frac{1}{2\pi(200 \times 10^6)(50)(0.385 - 0.25)} \cong 118 \text{ pF}$$

The reciprocal of point 3 is $1 - j2.1$ at point 4. From (19), the inductance is

$$L = \frac{50}{2\pi(200 \times 10^6)(2.1)} \cong 19 \text{ nH}$$

The inherent bandwidth of the conjugate-matched input circuit is found to be $3.62(BW)^i_{\text{out}}$ so that the overall bandwidth and selectivity of the amplifier are determined primarily by the output circuit.

The circuit diagram is shown in Fig. 3-6b. The capacitances in the ell-sections generally are not standard values, so variables in the desired capacitance range are usually used. The inductance can be adjusted by

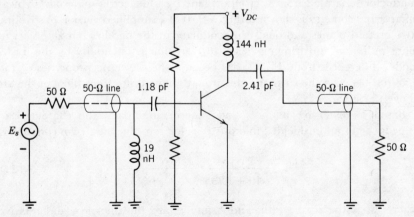

Figure 3-6b. Circuit for the amplifier in Example 3-3.

moving one or more turns physically, or by inserting a variable capacitor in series with a slightly larger inductance than required. Then adjusting the series capacitance effectively varies the inductance to the proper value.

The selectivity of a single-tuned amplifier is generally rather poor. Selectivity is improved by using several cascaded stages, single-tuned or double-tuned combinations that are synchronously tuned or stagger tuned.

3-21 Other Useful Matching Networks

Both of the elements in the ell network must be adjustable in order to compensate for measurement and calculation errors, and stray capacitances, and to "tweak up" the circuit for maximum power gain. In the tapped-capacitor circuit shown in Fig. 3-7a, transformable normalized input admittances can be located anywhere on the Smith chart *except* for the circular region inside the $g = 1$ circle. The actual inductance is not critical; the two adjustable capacitors provide the necessary compensation. Typical use is shown in Fig. 3-8.

The pi-section network of Fig. 3-7c has the desirable feature that all points on the Smith chart are transformable. It is often used in transmitters, but generally requires an additional DC blocking capacitor and an RF choke to supply the DC bias.

3-3 MICROSTRIP

When the frequency of operation is sufficiently high, the use of transmission-line sections as network elements becomes practical because of the short lengths required. Although several different types are available, the transmission line called microstrip is one of the most useful of all types.

Microstrip is a type of planar transmission line consisting of a single strip conductor separated from a ground plane by a dielectric material. Typical microstrip geometry is shown in Fig. 3-9. It is a simplified version of stripline (two ground planes and one strip conductor in the middle) but is subject to more radiation and fringing fields. Propagation is essentially by the TEM mode; differences from TEM arise because the dielectric properties of the material between the strip and the ground plane differ from those of the air above the strip.

Based on extensive analysis and experimental data, the characteristic impedance of an unshielded microstrip is, for zero-thickness strip conductor,

$$Z_o = \frac{377}{\sqrt{\epsilon_r}} \frac{h}{W} \frac{1}{\left[1 + 1.735 \epsilon_r^{-0.0724} (W/h)^{-0.836} \right]} \tag{23}$$

where W is the strip width, and h and ϵ_r are the thickness and relative dielectric constant of the dielectric substrate. The insulating dielectric provides most of the necessary structural strength for the microstrip.

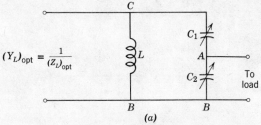

$$(Y_L)_{\text{opt}} = \frac{1}{(Z_L)_{\text{opt}}}$$

Figure 3-7a.   The tapped-capacitor matching network.

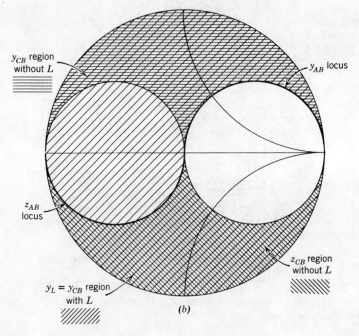

Figure 3-7b.   Matchable regions for the tapped-capacitor network. Any yl inside the $g = 1$ circle cannot be obtained.

Since the strip conductor has a nonzero thickness t, the width W in (23) is replaced by an effective width given by

$$W_{\text{eff}} = W + \frac{t}{\pi}\left(\ln\frac{2h}{t} + 1\right) \tag{24}$$

The wavelength λ_m for the microstrip line differs from the wavelength λ_{TEM} for the TEM mode because of the type of construction and the TEM wavelength differs from the free-space wavelength λ_o because of the relative dielectric constant of the insulator. The relationships are, for zero-thickness

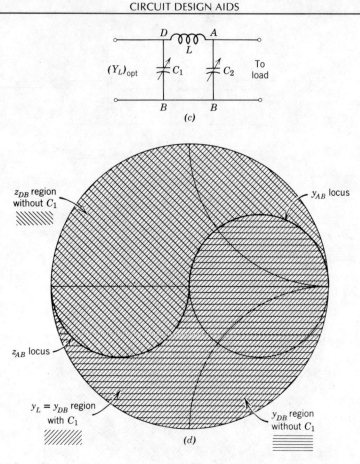

Figure 3-7c. *The pi-section matching network. (d) The matchable region for the pi-section network; covering the entire Smith chart.*

strip conductor,

$$\frac{\lambda_m}{\lambda_{\text{TEM}}} = \left[\frac{1}{1 + 0.63(\epsilon_r - 1)(W/h)^{0.1255}} \right]^{1/2} \quad \text{for} \quad \frac{W}{h} \geqslant 0.6 \quad (25a)$$

$$= \left[\frac{\epsilon_r}{1 + 0.6(\epsilon_r - 1)(W/h)^{0.0297}} \right]^{1/2} \quad \text{for} \quad \frac{W}{h} \leqslant 0.6 \quad (25b)$$

$$\lambda_{\text{TEM}} = \frac{\lambda_o}{\sqrt{\epsilon_r}} \quad\quad (25c)$$

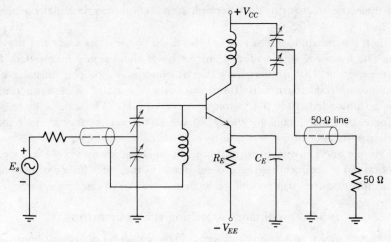

Figure 3-8.   Typical circuit using tapped-capacitor matching networks.

where λ_o is the free-space wavelength. The effective width must be used for nonzero thickness t of the strip conductor. In practice both the strip conductor and the ground plane do not need to be more than about four skin depths thick. This means that thick films up to 10 μ thickness are required. Such films can be produced by vacuum evaporation and sputtering, or by nonvacuum methods such as silk screening and vapor plating.

Hybrid microwave integrated circuits are often fabricated on ceramic substrates such as alumina (Al_2O_3) with $\epsilon_r = 9.9$, and $h = 25$ mils. The strip conductor is gold and most of the attenuation is conductor loss, with little loss attributed to the dielectric. Thick-dielectric microstrip has less loss than

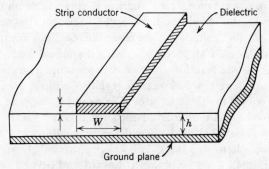

Figure 3-9.   Microstrip geometry.

thin-dielectric microstrip. Both ceramic and Teflon-fiberglass dielectrics are low loss.

When a semiconductor is used as the dielectric, its losses are not negligible. The loss in a semiconductor microstrip is significantly larger than for the ceramic or Teflon-fiberglass dielectric microstrip. Silicon must have a resistivity of 1500 Ω-cm and 10-mil thickness, for a 50-Ω $\lambda/4$ resonator to have an unloaded Q of 50 at a frequency of 10 GHz. This can be increased by increasing the silicon thickness, but the advantage is offset by increased thermal resistance and size of the monolithic distributed circuit.

A simple and convenient transition from 50-Ω microstrip to 50-Ω coax can be obtained by connecting the ground plane to the outer flange of the coax connector, and the strip conductor to the center tab of the connector.

3-31 Immittance Matching With Microstrip

The immittance transforming property of transmission lines is well known. A length of microstrip, aided by a shorted or open-circuited stub, is capable of transforming a 50-Ω load resistance into any value that can be represented on the usual Smith chart. Microstrip matching elements are convenient to use when the frequency is sufficiently high and the wavelength on the microstrip sufficiently short to make the lengths involved practical.

The input immittance is found as demonstrated in Example 3-2. It should be emphasized that the starting point for input admittance is diametrically opposite the starting point for input impedance. For example, suppose the input admittance is to be found for a shorted stub. Since for a short, $Z_R/Z_o = 0$ and $Y_R/Y_o = \infty$, enter the chart at ∞. Then move around the chart clockwise a distance in wavelengths equal to the stub length, and read the normalized input admittance. Notice that for stubs less than $\lambda/4$ long, the input admittance is inductive susceptance. For an open-circuited stub, $Y_R/Y_o = 0$, so that the input admittance of open-circuited stubs less than $\lambda/4$ long is capacitive susceptance. If attenuation is appreciable on the stubs, the radius at the end point should be decreased an amount that corresponds to the total loss in decibels, similar to the lossy-line case in Example 3-2.

It is usual to place a stub in parallel with the actual load. This parallel combination acts as the load for a section of microstrip. The stub length and the microstrip line length are chosen such that the input immitance of the microstrip line equals the desired value. For example, suppose 50 Ω is to be transformed into the optimum load admittance at point A in Fig. 3-10. Point O corresponds to the 50-Ω load normalized by dividing by 50Ω. When a shorted stub less than $\lambda/4$ long is placed in parallel with the $1+j0$ normalized load, points can be obtained toward and beyond point P on the $g = 1$ circle. To determine how much inductive susceptance should be added on by the shorted stub, draw a circular arc from point A to where the arc

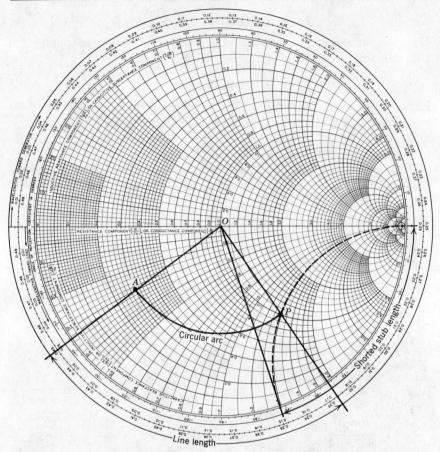

Figure 3-10. Construction for immittance matching with microstrip line and shorted stub.

crosses the $g=1$ circle. This intersection locates P and also indicates how long in wavelengths a lossless line should be to obtain an input admittance at A.

If stub and line losses are appreciable, the radii must be adjusted accordingly. If loss is too high, difficulty may be encountered if point A is near the outer edge of the Smith chart. In any case, it is desirable to minimize loss by using stub types and line lengths whose total length is minimum. This is also desirable from the construction and space standpoint. The circular arc AP in Fig. 3-10 also crosses the upper half of the $g=1$ circle. An open stub is the shorter one for this case compared to the length of shorted stub required and of course the line length is greater.

Example 3-4

Design input and output microstrip matching networks for the amplifier of Example 3-3.

Solution

Locate $(y_L)_{opt} = 0.0235 - j0.12$ on the Smith chart. Shortest total length of line plus stub is obtained by drawing a circular arc through $(y_L)_{opt}$ and the lower half of the $g = 1$ circle. The line length is found to be 0.206λ and the shorted stub is 0.026λ as shown in Fig. 3-11.

Next locate $(y_s)_{opt} = 1.88 - j2.65$. Shortest total length is obtained by drawing the circular arc through $(y_s)_{opt}$ and the upper half of the $g = 1$

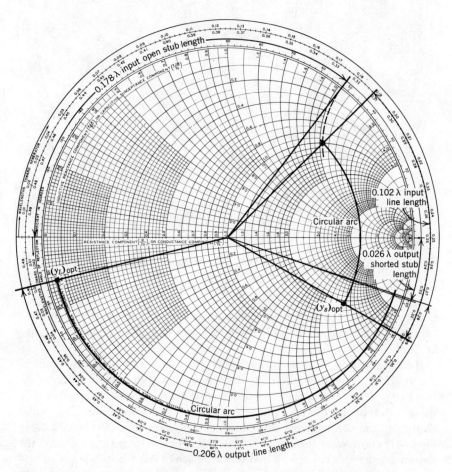

Figure 3-11.   Construction for Example 3-4.

circle. An open stub is considerably shorter than a shorted stub in this case. The line length is 0.102λ and the open-stub length is 0.178λ.

Suppose the microstrip is fabricated from 1/16-in. Teflon-impregnated fiberglass printed-circuit board, and that the constants are such that

$$\lambda_m = (0.7)\lambda_o \tag{26}$$

Since the frequency is 200 MHz, $\lambda_o = 150$ cm. Although this frequency is not high enough for microstrip matching to be seriously considered, the solution will be continued because it illustrates the design procedure. From (26)

$$\lambda_m = 105 \text{ cm}$$

The output line length is 21.6 cm, the shorted output stub is 2.73 cm, the input line length is 10.7 cm, and the open input stub is 18.7 cm.

A circuit diagram for the proposed amplifier is shown in Fig. 3-12. Feedthrough bypass capacitors C_2 provide the AC shorts for the output stub and the λ/4 bias line.

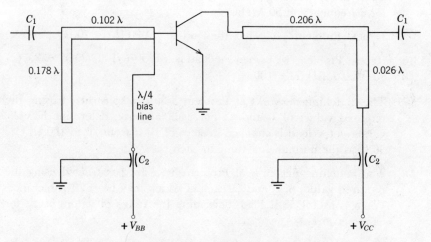

Figure 3-12. Transistor amplifier with microstrip matching networks.

PROBLEMS

3-1. Determine the reactances needed in two types of ell matching networks to convert a 50-Ω load into

$$Y_L = (3.3 - j4.4)10^{-3}$$

3-2.   Determine the reactances needed in two types of ell matching networks to convert a 50-Ω source into

$$Y_s = (8.6 - j12.9)10^{-3}$$

3-3.   Design two ell matching networks to change a 50-Ω load into each of the following:

   (a) $Y_L = (8 - j20)10^{-3}$

   (b) $Y_L = (8 + j20)10^{-3}$

Draw the circuit diagram and specify values of L and C in each case for a frequency of 50 MHz.

3-4.   Design two ell matching networks to change a 50-Ω source into each of the following:

   (a) $Y_s = (40 - j20)10^{-3}$

   (b) $Y_s = (40 + j20)10^{-3}$

Draw the circuit diagram and specify values of L and C in each case for a frequency of 50 MHz.

3-5.   Repeat Problem 3-3a when the load is: (a) 30 Ω (b) 70 Ω.

3-6.   Repeat Problem 3-3a when the load is: (a) $50 + j100$, (b) $50 - j25$, (c) $50 - j60.5$, (d) $50 - j100$.

3-7.   The matching networks of Problem 3-3a are constructed using the required values of L and C. For each network, determine how Y_L varies as the load is changed in steps of 10 Ω from 20 to 100 Ω. Use 50 Ω as the normalizing value in each case.

3-8.   The matching networks of Problem 3-3a are constructed using the required values of L and C, each of which may be $\pm 20\%$ tolerance. For a constant 50-Ω load, determine the range of values of Y_L for each network.

3-9.   The matching networks of Problem 3-3a are constructed using the values of L and C required at 50 MHz. For each network, determine how Y_L varies as the frequency is changed in steps of 5 MHz from 35 to 65 MHz.

3-10. The CE parameters of the 2N743 at 60 MHz are

$$y_{ie} = (6.8 + j6.1)10^{-3} \qquad y_{re} = (-j0.81)10^{-3}$$

$$y_{fe} = (33.6 - j44.2)10^{-3} \qquad y_{oe} = (1.24 + j1.92)10^{-3}$$

The transistor is to be used as a CE amplifier between 50-Ω terminations. The input and output circuits each are to have identical bandwidths of 2 MHz. Select and design suitable ell matching networks to provide suitable terminations for the transistor. Draw a schematic diagram showing how you would connect the matching networks. Include all DC source connections and bias circuits, coupling and bypass capacitors, and RF chokes. Specify values of components where possible. What power gain in decibels would you expect? What is the overall bandwidth? What is the tunability factor?

3-11. The CE parameters of a transistor at 450 MHz are

$$y_{ie} = (29.7 + j14.3)10^{-3} \qquad y_{re} = (-0.38 - j2)10^{-3}$$

$$y_{fe} = (-10.3 - j50.2)10^{-3} \qquad y_{oe} = (0.93 + j5.31)10^{-3}$$

The transistor is to be used in a CE amplifier between 50-Ω terminations. The output circuit is to have a bandwidth of 45 MHz. Design the matching networks to provide maximum power gain and maximum output power. What power gain in decibels would you expect? What is the bandwidth of the input circuit? What is the tunability factor?

3-12. Design matching networks using 50-Ω strip lines and stubs to convert 50-Ω terminations into

$$(a) \qquad Y_L = (0.47 - j2.4)10^{-3}$$

$$(b) \qquad Y_s = (37.6 - j53)10^{-3}$$

Specify lengths in wavelengths.

3-13. Design 50-Ω strip line and stub matching networks for a 450 MHz amplifier using the transistor parameters of Problem 3-11. Ignore bandwidth and lineloss considerations. The matching networks are to convert 50-Ω terminations into the optimum terminations required by the transistor. Assume that the wavelength on the strip lines and stubs is 0.8 of the wavelength in free space. Draw the circuit diagram, specify lengths in centimeters, and show how you would supply DC to the transistor.

CHAPTER FOUR

UNILATERAL AMPLIFIERS

4-0 INTRODUCTION

A device is unilateral if its reverse transmission parameter is zero. Also, if the generalized parameter $k_r = 0$, and if $\text{Re}(k_i) > 0$ and $\text{Re}(k_o) > 0$, the device is inherently stable. An amplifier that uses a unilateral device is also unilateral if there is no feedback external to the device. An amplifier that uses a nonunilateral device is also nonunilateral unless there is external feedback that neutralizes the effect of feedback internal to the device.

Not only is the unilateral amplifier desirable because of its inherent stability, but also because its input and output circuits are completely decoupled except for the forward direction parameter k_f. Therefore the tunability factor δ is zero. Also, values for the optimum terminations, power gains, and bandwidths are more easily determined for unilateral than for nonunilateral amplifiers if the device parameters are known.

Unfortunately, most devices are nonunilateral, particularly at high frequencies. There are schemes, however, whereby external circuitry can be used to effectively neutralize the internal feedback of the device so as to make the overall circuit unilateral in operation.

4-1 THE CASCODE CIRCUIT

Two transistors connected CE-CB as shown in Fig. 4-1 is called a cascode. It has properties of a unilateral device. Let the y parameters of the CE transistor be represented by y_{ie}, y_{re}, y_{fe}, and y_{oe}, and of the CB transistor by y_{ib},

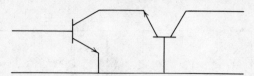

Figure 4-1. The CE-CB or cascode circuit.

y_{rb}, y_{fb}, and y_{ob}. Then the overall parameters of the cascode are given by

$$y_{11} = \frac{y_{ie}(y_{oe}+y_{ib}) - y_{fe}y_{re}}{y_{oe}+y_{ib}} \cong y_{ie} \tag{1}$$

$$y_{12} = -\frac{y_{re}y_{rb}}{y_{oe}+y_{ib}} \cong 0 \tag{2}$$

$$y_{21} = -\frac{y_{fe}y_{fb}}{y_{oe}+y_{ib}} \cong -y_{fe} \tag{3}$$

$$y_{22} = \frac{y_{ob}(y_{oe}+y_{ib}) - y_{rb}y_{fb}}{y_{oe}+y_{ib}} \cong y_{ob} \tag{4}$$

In (1), $y_{fe}y_{re}$ is small compared to the first term so that y_{11} is approximated by y_{ie} of the first transistor. In (2), the product of two reverse transmission parameters each of which can be small, results in y_{12} being sufficiently small that it is difficult to measure. In (3) and (4), the parameters are such that y_{21} is nearly the same as $-y_{fe}$ for the first transistor, and y_{22} is nearly the same as y_{ob} for the second transistor. Therefore, since $y_{12} \cong 0$, the cascode acts like a unilateral device. The resulting equivalent circuit is shown in Fig. 4-2. Since $y_{12} \cong 0$, the input admittance is

$$Y_{in} = y_{11} = g_{11} + jb_{11} \tag{5}$$

and the output admittance is

$$Y_{out} = y_{22} = g_{22} + jb_{22} \tag{6}$$

Then the operating power gain becomes

$$G_p = \frac{|V_2|^2 G_L}{|V_1|^2 G_{in}} = |A_v|^2 \frac{G_L}{g_{11}} = \frac{|y_{21}|^2 G_L}{|y_{22} + Y_L|^2 g_{11}} \tag{7}$$

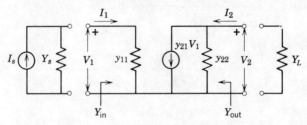

Figure 4-2.   The y-parameter equivalent circuit for the cascode arrangement.

provided $g_{11} > 0$ and $g_{22} > 0$, that is, the circuit is inherently stable. Maximum operating power gain is obtained when (7) is maximized, and this occurs when

$$(Y_L)_{\text{opt}} = y_{22}^* \tag{8}$$

so that the maximum operating power gain is

$$G_{p_{\text{max}}} = \frac{|y_{21}|^2 g_{22}}{4 g_{22}^2 g_{11}} = \frac{|y_{21}|^2}{4 g_{11} g_{22}} \tag{9}$$

Maximum input power occurs when

$$(Y_s)_{\text{opt}} = y_{11}^* \tag{10}$$

Example   4-1

At 60 MHz, the Motorola MC 1550 integrated cascode has the parameters

$$y_{11} = (2.5 + j2.3)10^{-3} \qquad y_{12} \cong 0$$
$$y_{21} = (10 - j19)10^{-3} \qquad y_{22} = (0.01 + j0.8)10^{-3}$$

Determine: (*a*) Optimum terminations; (*b*) maximum power gain.

Solution

(*a*) $(Y_s)_{\text{opt}} = y_{11}^* = (2.5 - j2.3)10^{-3}$, which is inductive, and

$$(Y_L)_{\text{opt}} = y_{22}^* = (0.01 - j0.8)10^{-3}$$

which is also inductive. Both y_{11} and y_{22} are capacitive.

$$(b) \qquad G_{p_{\text{max}}} = \frac{|y_{21}|^2}{4 g_{11} g_{22}} = \frac{|10 - j19|^2}{4 \times 2.5 \times 0.01} = 4610 \cong 37\,dB$$

The input circuit becomes that shown in Fig. 4-3, in which
$G = 2g_{11} = 5 \times 10^{-3}$ mho, $C = 2.3 \times 10^{-3}/\omega = 6.1$ pF, and
$L = 1.15 \mu$H. The output circuit has
$G = 2g_{22} = 0.02 \times 10^{-3}$ mho, $C = 0.8 \times 10^{-3}/\omega = 2.12$ pF, and
$L = 3.32 \mu$H.

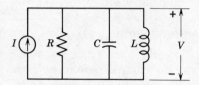

Figure 4-3. *Parallel RLC tuned circuit connected to a constant-current source.*

4-2 SOME CIRCUIT RELATIONSHIPS

4-21 Q

The seventeenth letter of the alphabet was originally used in 1920 simply to designate the ratio of reactance magnitude to effective series resistance of a coil (now called an inductor). Subsequently, Q was applied to both coils and condensers (now called capacitors) and attempts were made to introduce names like dissipation constant, quality factor, storage factor, and figure of merit for Q. Do not confuse this use of Q with that introduced in 2-12.

Later, Q was found to be useful when applied to a resonant circuit and was related to what was called sharpness of resonance. Then Q was related to logarithmic decrement, which was defined as the natural logarithm of the ratio of two successive maxima in a damped oscillation such as produced in a spark gap wireless transmitter. The number of complete oscillations required to obtain a certain ratio of initial to final amplitudes is Q/π times the natural logarithm of that ratio.

Then it was found that Q could be given a physical interpretation for a simple resonant circuit. Thus Q became equal to 2π times the ratio of maximum energy stored in either the inductor or capacitor to the energy dissipated per cycle.

Still later, it was found that Q was related to the shape of a curve representing the magnitude of impedance or admittance of a single-resonant circuit plotted against frequency. Hence Q became equal to the ratio of resonant frequency to the width of the curve between the frequencies on either side of the resonant frequency, where the magnitude of the curve is $1/\sqrt{2}$ times the maximum or $\sqrt{2}$ times the minimum magnitude. The width of the curve became known as bandwidth, and the frequencies on either side of the resonant frequency are called half-power points for which the response differs from that of resonance by 3 dB.

Q can be applied to any type of resonant device or structure where energy storage and energy dissipation or a resonant response occurs. Thus Q can have meaning with piezoelectric crystals, resonant transmission lines, cavity resonators, magnetic and dielectric materials, radiation owing to transitions between atomic or molecular energy states, bouncing balls, rotating bodies such as a gyroscope or the planet Earth, pendulums, organ pipes, piano strings, and auditoriums as well as inductors and capacitors.

4-22 Series-Parallel Transformations

A circuit composed of an inductor or capacitor, whose reactance magnitude is X_1 and whose resistance is R_x, in series with an external resistance R_1 can be transformed into an equivalent parallel circuit composed of resistance R_2 and reactance magnitude X_2 as illustrated in Fig. 4-4. The required values of R_2 and X_2 are obtained by first equating the impedances. Thus

$$(R_1 + R_x) + jX_1 = \frac{R_2(jX_2)}{R_2 + jX_2} = \frac{R_2 X_2^2}{R_2^2 + X_2^2} + j\frac{R_2^2 X_2}{R_2^2 + X_2^2} \tag{11}$$

Therefore

$$R_1 + R_x = \frac{R_2 X_2^2}{R_2^2 + X_2^2} \tag{12}$$

and

$$X_1 = \frac{R_2^2 X_2}{R_2^2 + X_2^2} \tag{13}$$

If X_1 is inductive, X_2 in inductive, and if X_1 is capacitive, X_2 is capacitive.

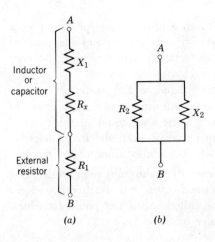

Figure 4-4. (a) Series circuit. (b) Equivalent parallel circuit.

The series circuit has an overall Q given by

$$Q_1 = \frac{X_1}{R_1 + R_x} \tag{14}$$

and the inductor or capacitor has its own Q given by

$$Q_x = \frac{X_1}{R_x} \tag{15}$$

Divide (13) by (12) to obtain

$$Q_1 = \frac{X_1}{R_1 + R_x} = \frac{R_2}{X_2} \tag{16}$$

which indicates that the overall Q of the series circuit is also given by the ratio of the equivalent *parallel* resistance to the equivalent *parallel* reactance.

Rearranging (12) and using (14) give

$$R_1 + R_x = \frac{R_2}{1 + (R_2/X_2)^2} = \frac{R_2}{1 + Q_1^2} \tag{17}$$

from which is obtained

$$R_2 = (R_1 + R_x)(1 + Q_1^2) \tag{18}$$

This indicates that a series resistance $(R_1 + R_x)$ is transformed into a larger value R_2 by the factor $(1 + Q_1^2)$.

Rearranging (13) and using (16) gives

$$X_1 = \frac{X_2}{1 + (X_2/R_2)^2} = \frac{X_2}{1 + 1/Q_1^2} \tag{19}$$

from which is obtained

$$X_2 = X_1\left(1 + \frac{1}{Q_1^2}\right) \tag{20}$$

Therefore the equivalent parallel reactance X_2 is larger than the series reactance X_1 by the factor $(1 + 1/Q_1^2)$.

If Q_1 is sufficiently high, say 10 or more, then

$$R_2 \cong (R_1 + R_x)Q_1^2 \tag{21}$$

and

$$X_2 \cong X_1 \tag{22}$$

Example 4-2

At 60 MHz, a 5-μH inductor has $Q_x = 200$. Find the equivalent parallel-circuit values (*a*) of the inductor alone, and (*b*) if a 50-Ω resistance is connected in series with the inductor.

Solution

(*a*) From (15), the resistance of the inductor is

$$R_x = \frac{X_1}{Q_x} = \frac{2\pi \times 60 \times 10^6 \times 5 \times 10^{-6}}{200} = \frac{377 \times 5}{200} \cong 9.4\,\Omega$$

From (14), with $R_1 = 0$, $Q_1 = Q_x = 200$. Thus the equivalent parallel resistance is, from (21),

$$R_2 = R_x Q_1^{\,2} = 377\,k\Omega$$

The equivalent parallel reactance is, from (16),

$$X_2 = \frac{R_2}{Q_1} = \frac{377\,k\Omega}{200} \cong 1.89\,k\Omega$$

or, from (22), $X_2 \cong X_1 = 377 \times 5 \cong 1.89\,k\Omega$
(*b*) Since now $R_1 = 50\,\Omega$, then from (14),

$$Q_1 = \frac{X_1}{R_1 + R_x} = \frac{377 \times 5}{50 + 9.4} = 31.7$$

Then, from (21),

$$R_2 \cong (R_1 + R_x)Q_1^{\,2} = 59.4 \times 31.7^2 = 59.8\,k\Omega$$

and X_2 is the same as before since Q_1 is still high.

Similarly, the 50-Ω series resistance alone transforms into $X_1^{\,2}/R_1 = 71.2\,k\Omega$ parallel resistance. Then $71.2\,k\Omega$ in parallel with $377\,k\Omega$ equals $59.8\,k\Omega$.

In some practical situations, the circuit designer may wish to transform a known R_1 into known values of R_2 and X_2 (or conductance $1/R_2$ and susceptance $1/X_2$) and needs to determine X_1 and the value of Q_x to strive for. Thus R_x should be eliminated in favor of Q_x. This can be done by solving (14) and (15) for R_x to obtain

$$R_x = \frac{R_1}{(Q_x/Q_1)-1} \tag{23}$$

Then substitute (23) into (18) and solve for Q_1. Then

$$Q_1 = -\frac{R_2}{2R_1Q_x} + \sqrt{\left(\frac{R_2}{2R_1Q_x}\right)^2 + \left(\frac{R_2}{R_1}-1\right)} \tag{24}$$

which indicates how Q_x affects the value of Q_1 required.

It can be shown that if

$$Q_x \gg \frac{R_2/R_1}{2\sqrt{(R_2/R_1)-1}} \tag{25}$$

then (24) becomes

$$Q_1 \cong \sqrt{\frac{R_2}{R_1}-1} \tag{26}$$

Furthermore, if $R_2/R_1 \gg 1$, (25) becomes

$$Q_x \gg \tfrac{1}{2}\sqrt{\frac{R_2}{R_1}} \tag{27}$$

which shows that as the resistance transformation ratio R_2/R_1 increases, Q_x must also increase in order for the resistance R_x to have negligible effect.

Example 4-3

Design an input matching network for the integrated cascode of Example 4-1 to transform a 50-Ω source resistance into the optimum termination $(Y_s)_{opt}$.

Solution 1

Since $(Y_s)_{opt} = (2.5 - j2.3)10^{-3}$, the 50-$\Omega$ source must be transformed into a resistance $1/g_{11} = 400\,\Omega$ in parallel with inductive susceptance $b_{11} = 2.3 \times 10^{-3}$ mho. So let $R_1 = 50\,\Omega$ and $R_2 = 400\,\Omega$. Then $R_2/R_1 = 8$, so if $Q_x \gg (R_2/R_1)/2\sqrt{(R_2/R_1)-1} = 8/2\sqrt{7} = 1.51$, or if $Q_x \geqslant 20(1.51) \cong 30$ (for example), the resistance of the series inductor L_1 has little effect. Thus, whatever value L_1 turns out to be, its $Q_x \geqslant 30$ provides a practical goal to strive for. Otherwise, (24) must be used to find Q_1. Assume $Q_x \geqslant 30$ can be attained. Then, from (26),

$$Q_1 \cong \sqrt{\frac{R_2}{R_1} - 1} = \sqrt{7} = 2.64$$

and from (23),

$$R_x = \frac{R_1}{(Q_x/Q_1) - 1} = \frac{50}{10.4} = 4.8\,\Omega$$

Then $X_1 = \omega L_1 = R_1 Q_1 = 50 \times 2.64 = 132\,\Omega$ and $L_1 = X_1/\omega = 132/377 \times 10^6 = 0.35\,\mu H$. Also $X_2 = X_1(1 + 1/Q_1^2) = 132[1 + 1/(2.64)^2] = 151\,\Omega$, which corresponds to inductive susceptance $1/151 = 6.63 \times 10^{-3}$ mho. Since this is larger than the inductive susceptance of 2.3×10^{-3} mho desired, the capacitive susceptance $B_c = (6.63 - 2.3)10^{-3} = 4.33 \times 10^{-3}$ mho must be added across terminals $A - B$ in Fig. 4-5. The parallel capacitance is $4.33 \times 10^{-3}/377 \times 10^6 = 11.5\,pF$.

Appropriate matching can also be obtained if $X_1 = 132\,\Omega$ is capacitive instead of inductive. This means that additional inductive susceptance of 8.93×10^{-3} mho must be added across terminals $A - B$ in order to obtain the desired $(Y_s)_{opt} = (2.5 - j2.3)10^{-3}$ mho. In this case the series capacitance is $1/\omega X_1 \cong 20\,pF$ and the parallel inductance needed is $0.297\,\mu H$.

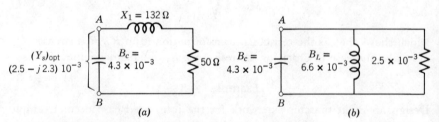

Figure 4-5. (a) A matching network for Example 4-3. (b) Equivalent parallel circuit.

Solution 2   Using the Smith Chart

The normalized termination $y_s = 50(2.5 - j2.3)10^{-3} = (0.125 - j0.115)$ is to be obtained from a normalized source impedance $(50 + j0)/50 = 1 + j0$. Inductive reactance can be added in series with $1 + j0$ to yield point A at $1 + j2.63$ in Fig. 4-6. Thus $X_1/50 = 2.63$, or $X_1 = 132\,\Omega$. The reciprocal of

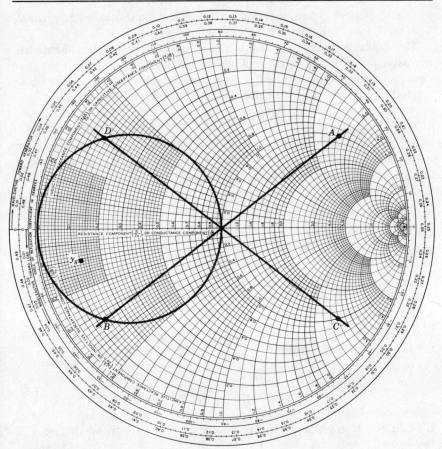

Figure 4-6.   Construction for Example 4-3.

point A gives a normalized admittance at point B equal to $0.125 - j0.33$. So the normalized capacitive susceptance of $(0.33 - 0.115) = 0.215$ added to point B results in the desired y_s. Since $50\omega C = 0.215$, the required parallel capacitive susceptance is $\omega C = 0.215/50 = 4.3 \times 10^{-3}$ mho.

Another possibility is to add capacitive reactance in series with $1 + j0$ to obtain point C at $1 - j2.3$. Again $X_1 = 132\,\Omega$, but now it is capacitive. The reciprocal of point C gives normalized admittance at point D equal to $0.125 + j0.33$. Thus normalized inductive susceptance equal to $(0.33 + 0.115) = 0.445$ added to point D results in the desired y_s. Since $50/\omega L = 0.445$, the required parallel inductive susceptance is $1/\omega L = 0.445/50 = 8.9 \times 10^{-3}$ mho.

The numerical values obtained by using the Smith chart agree closely with those from Solution 1.

This example illustrates that if two conditions are imposed on the matching network, for example, the real and imaginary parts of y_s, then only two elements are generally required in the matching network. If three conditions are to be met, the matching network will require three elements.

4-3 BANDWIDTH CONSIDERATIONS

When a conjugate match is used in either the input or output circuit, the result can be considered to be as illustrated in Fig. 4-3. The total admittance of the parallel combination is

$$Y = G + j(B_c - B_L) \tag{28}$$

where $G = 1/R$, $B_c = \omega C$, and $B_L = 1/(\omega L)$.
Then

$$|Y| = \sqrt{G^2 + (B_c - B_L)^2} \tag{29}$$

Since $V = I/Y$, the voltage across G is inversely proportional to Y; therefore the power delivered to G is

$$P = |V|^2 G = \frac{|I|^2 G}{G^2 + (B_c - B_L)^2} = \frac{|I|^2}{G\{1 + [(B_c - B_L)/G]^2\}} \tag{30}$$

If G, L, and C are independent of frequency, the power is maximized at a frequency f_0 for which

$$(B_c)_{f_0} = (B_L)_{f_0} \tag{31}$$

Then

$$\omega_0 C = \frac{1}{\omega_0 L} \tag{32}$$

or

$$\omega_0^2 LC = 1 \tag{33}$$

and the maximum power is

$$P_{max} = \frac{|I|^2}{G} \tag{34}$$

Thus (30) can be written as

$$P = \frac{P_{max}}{1 + [(B_c - B_L)/G]^2} = \frac{P_{max}}{1 + \left[\left(\omega C - \frac{1}{\omega L}\right)/G\right]^2} \tag{35}$$

At frequency f_1 below f_0 for which

$$\frac{1}{\omega_1 L} - \omega_1 C = G \tag{36}$$

and at frequency f_2 above f_0 for which

$$\omega_2 C - \frac{1}{\omega_2 L} = G \tag{37}$$

the power becomes $P_{max}/2$, a decrease of 3 dB. If the power is halved, then $|V|$ becomes $1/\sqrt{2} = 0.707$ of its value at f_0, and this also is a decrease of 3 dB. Hence bandwidth is defined to be

$$BW = f_2 - f_1 \text{ Hz} \tag{38}$$

Bandwidth can be expressed in terms of circuit constants by solving (36) for ω_1 to obtain

$$\omega_1 = \frac{-G}{2C} + \sqrt{\left(\frac{G}{2C}\right)^2 + \frac{1}{LC}} \tag{39}$$

and solving (37) for ω_2 to obtain

$$\omega_2 = \frac{G}{2C} + \sqrt{\left(\frac{G}{2C}\right)^2 + \frac{1}{LC}} \tag{40}$$

Then

$$BW = \frac{\omega_2 - \omega_1}{2\pi} = \frac{G}{2\pi C} = \frac{f_0 G}{2\pi f_0 C} = \frac{f_0}{Q_c} \tag{41}$$

where

$$Q_c = \frac{2\pi f_0 C}{G} = \frac{R}{\omega_0 L} = \frac{1}{\omega_0 L G}$$

is the Q of the entire circuit.

Observe that when (39) and (40) are multiplied, $\omega_1\omega_2 = 1/LC = \omega_0^2$, or

$$f_0 = \sqrt{f_1 f_2} \tag{42}$$

This means that f_0 is the geometric mean of f_1 and f_2, not the arithmetic mean.

The arithmetic mean occurs when $f_0 = \frac{1}{2}(f_1 + f_2)$ or $\omega_0 = \frac{1}{2}(\omega_1 + \omega_2)$. To see if this can be obtained, add (39) and (40) and divide by 2. Thus

$$\frac{\omega_1 + \omega_2}{2} = \sqrt{\left(\frac{G}{2C}\right)^2 + \frac{1}{LC}} = \omega_0 \sqrt{1 + \frac{1}{4Q_c^2}} \tag{43}$$

Thus, if $Q_c \geqslant 10$, $\sqrt{1 + 1/4Q_c^2} \leqslant \sqrt{1.0025} \cong 1$, then f_0 is essentially halfway between f_1 and f_2.

Example 4-4

Determine the bandwidths of the conjugate matched input and output circuits of the integrated cascode of Example 4-1.

Solution

The bandwidth for conjugate matched circuits is called the inherent bandwidth. For the output circuit,

$$(BW)_{\text{out}}^i = \frac{f_0}{Q_c} = \frac{f_0}{R/\omega_0 L} = \frac{f_0}{b_{22}/2g_{22}}$$

$$= \frac{60 \times 10^6}{0.8 \times 10^{-3}/(2 \times 0.01 \times 10^{-3})} = \frac{60}{40} \text{ MHz}$$

$$= 1.5 \text{ MHz}$$

For the input circuit,

$$(BW)_{\text{in}}^i = \frac{f_0}{b_{11}/2g_{11}} = \frac{60 \times 10^6}{2.3 \times 10^{-3}/2 \times 2.5 \times 10^{-3}}$$

$$= \frac{60}{0.46} \text{ MHz} = 130 \text{ MHz}!$$

Such a large value may not be obtained in the actual circuit because of the variation of C_{11} and g_{11} with frequency. It can be expected, however, that $(BW)^i_{in} > (BW)^i_{out}$.

4-4 OPTIMUM TERMINATIONS WITH SPECIFIED BANDWIDTH

In order to decrease bandwidth below the value normally obtained with a conjugate match, the circuit Q must be increased. This can be done in the input circuit, for example, by adding capacitor C_s across the input circuit. Then the additional capacitive susceptance $\omega_0 C_s$ can be considered to be part of the capacitive susceptance b_{11} of the device. The circuit Q becomes

$$Q_c = \frac{b_{11} + \omega_0 C_s}{2g_{11}} \tag{44}$$

and this is related to the specified decreased bandwidth by

$$Q_c = \frac{f_0}{BW_{in}} \tag{45}$$

From (44) and (45) the total capacitive susceptance, considered to be a new value of the b_{11} parameter, is found to be

$$b_{11}' = b_{11} + \omega_0 C_s = \frac{2g_{11} f_0}{BW_{in}} \tag{46}$$

The inherent bandwidth of the input circuit is obtained with $C_s = 0$. Thus

$$(BW)^i_{in} = \frac{2g_{11} f_0}{b_{11}} \tag{47}$$

and (46) becomes

$$b_{11}' = b_{11} + \omega_0 C_s = b_{11} \frac{(BW)^i_{in}}{BW_{in}} \tag{48}$$

To obtain a conjugate match also, the input matching network must provide simultaneously an inductive susceptance magnitude b_{11}' and a parallel conductance g_{11}. Therefore, the optimum source admittance for specified bandwidth becomes

$$(Y_s)_{opt}^{BW} = g_{11} - jb_{11}' \tag{49}$$

Then, from (46) or (48), the additional capacitance necessary is

$$C_s = \frac{1}{2\pi}\left(\frac{2g_{11}}{BW_{in}} - \frac{b_{11}}{f_0}\right) = \frac{b_{11}}{\omega_0}\left[\frac{(BW)^i_{in}}{BW_{in}} - 1\right] \qquad (50)$$

If b_{11} of the device is inductive susceptance rather than capacitive susceptance, then additional inductive susceptance magnitude $1/\omega_0 L_s$ can be added across the input circuit to decrease bandwidth. Hence, for this case,

$$b'_{11} = b_{11} + \frac{1}{\omega_0 L_s} = \frac{2g_{11}f_0}{BW_{in}} = b_{11}\frac{(BW)^i_{in}}{BW_{in}} \qquad (51)$$

The additional inductance is

$$L_s = \frac{1}{\omega_0(2g_{11}f_0/BW_{in} - b_{11})} = \frac{1}{\omega_0 b_{11}\left[(BW)^i_{in}/BW_{in} - 1\right]} \qquad (52)$$

and the optimum source termination is

$$(Y_s)_{opt}^{BW} = g_{11} + jb'_{11} \qquad (53)$$

Similar relationships for the output circuit are readily obtained in terms of g_{22}, b_{22}, f_0, $(BW)^i_{out}$, BW_{out}, b'_{22}, C_L, and $(Y_L)_{opt}^{BW}$. (See Problem 4-3.)

Example 4-5

Design an input matching network for the integrated cascode of Example 4-3 to provide an input circuit bandwidth of 1.5 MHz.

Solution

Since, from Example 4-4, $(BW)^i_{in} = 130$ MHz, then

$$b'_{11} = b_{11} + \omega_0 C_s = b_{11}\frac{(BW)^i_{in}}{BW_{in}}$$

$$= 2.3 \times 10^{-3} \times \frac{130}{1.5} = 200 \times 10^{-3}\,\text{mho}$$

$$\omega_0 C_s = b'_{11} - b_{11} = 200 \times 10^{-3} - 2.3 \times 10^{-3}$$

$$= 197.7 \times 10^{-3}$$

$$C_s = \frac{197.7 \times 10^{-3}}{377 \times 10^6} = 525\,\text{pF}$$

The optimum source admittance is

$$(Y_s)_{opt}^{BW} = g_{11} - jb'_{11} = (2.5 - j200)10^{-3} \text{ mho}$$

The normalized termination

$$y_s^{BW} = 50(2.5 - j200)10^{-3} = (0.125 - j10)$$

is to be obtained from the normalized source impedance $(50 + j0)/50 = 1 + j0$.

One possible matching network adds normalized capacitive reactance in series with $1 + j0$ to obtain point A at $1 - j2.63$ in Fig. 4-7. So $X_1 = 1/\omega_0 C_1$

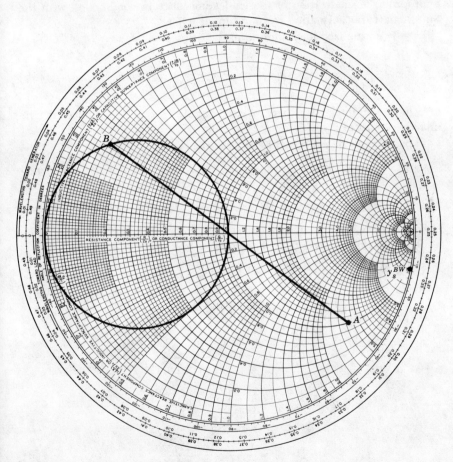

Figure 4-7. Construction for Example 4-5.

$=50(2.63)=132\,\Omega$. The reciprocal of point A gives normalized admittance at point B equal to $(0.125+0.33)$. Now, if normalized inductive susceptance equal to $(0.33+10)=10.33$ is added in parallel, then the desired $y_s{}^{BW}$ is obtained.

4-5 POWER GAIN REPRESENTED ON THE SMITH CHART

The operating power gain of a unilateral amplifier has been shown to be

$$G_p = \frac{|y_{21}|^2 G_L}{|y_{22}+Y_L|^2 g_{11}} \tag{54}$$

This can be conveniently represented on the Smith chart by using an appropriate normalization of the load admittance in conjunction with the Smith chart transformation relationship, as follows.

Let the normalized load admittance be defined as

$$y = g + jb = \frac{G_L}{g_{22}} + j\frac{B_L + b_{22}}{g_{22}} \tag{55}$$

in which the imaginary part of the parameter y_{22} is included in the imaginary part of y.

Thus (54) can be expressed as

$$G_p = \frac{|y_{21}|^2 g}{g_{11} g_{22}\left[(g+1)^2 + b^2\right]} \tag{56}$$

It has been shown that maximum power gain occurs when $B_L = -b_{22}$ (i.e., $b=0$) and $G_L = g_{22}$ (i.e., $g=1$). Therefore

$$G_{p_{\max}} = \frac{|y_{21}|^2}{4g_{11} g_{22}} \tag{57}$$

so that (56) becomes

$$G_p = 4G_{p_{\max}} \frac{g}{\left[(g+1)^2 + b^2\right]} \tag{58}$$

Let the Smith chart transformation be

$$U + jV = \frac{y-1}{y+1} = \frac{g-1+jb}{g+1+jb} \tag{59}$$

from which is obtained

$$U = \frac{g^2 - 1 + b^2}{(g+1)^2 + b^2} \quad \text{and} \quad V = \frac{2b}{(g+1)^2 + b^2} \tag{60}$$

Solving for g and b gives

$$g = \frac{1 - U^2 - V^2}{V^2 + (U-1)^2} = \frac{-2(U-1)}{V^2 + (U-1)^2} - 1 \quad \text{and} \quad b = \frac{2V}{V^2 + (U-1)^2} \tag{61}$$

To represent (58) on the Smith chart, eliminate g and b by using (61). The result is

$$U^2 + V^2 = \left[\sqrt{1 - \frac{G_p}{G_{p_{\max}}}} \right]^2 \tag{62}$$

which represents a family of circles in the $U - jV$ plane whose centers are at $U = 0$ and $V = 0$ (i.e., the origin of the Smith chart) and whose radii are given by

$$r = \sqrt{1 - \frac{G_p}{G_{p_{\max}}}} \tag{63}$$

The radii vary from $r = 0$ for $G_p = G_{p_{\max}}$ (the point for $g = 1$ and $b = 0$) to $r = 1$ for $G_p = 0$ (the outside circle for $g = 0$).

When a circle for a specified power gain ratio is drawn, the Smith chart coordinates for points on the circle represent all possible passive values of g and b; hence, G_L and B_L, which give the specified ratio.

Table 4-1 gives the radii of several circles in terms of the decibel decrease of G_p below $G_{p_{\max}}$ and the corresponding power gain ratios. Several circles are drawn in Fig. 4-8 and marked as negative decibels. They apply to any inherently stable unilateral device.

TABLE 4-1 VALUES OF r IN TERMS OF THE DECIBEL DECREASE BELOW $G_{p_{\max}}$

Decibel decrease	0	1	2	3	4	5	7	10
$G_p / G_{p_{\max}}$	1	0.795	0.63	0.5	0.398	0.316	0.199	0.1
r	0	0.453	0.608	0.707	0.776	0.827	0.895	0.949

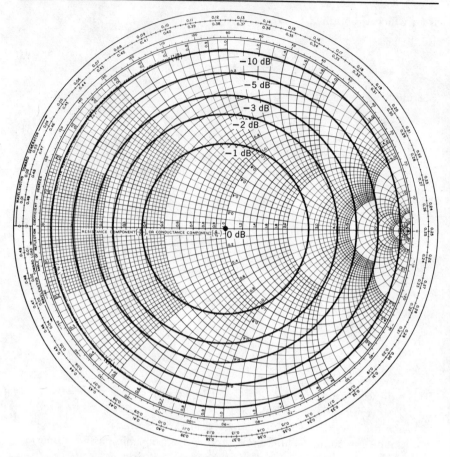

Figure 4-8.   Power-gain circles for the unilateral amplifier.

It is observed that considerable variation in load admittance from the optimum value is possible before the power gain drops by a given amount, say, 1 dB. For example, if $g = 0.5$, b can be anywhere from $+0.5$ to -0.5 and the power gain is within 1 dB of $G_{p_{max}}$. Or, if $g = 1.5$, b can be between $+1.14$ and -1.14 for the same 1 dB range.

4-6 VOLTAGE AND CURRENT GAINS REPRESENTED ON THE SMITH CHART

The voltage gain of an amplifier is given in Table 2-1 as

$$A_v = \frac{-y_f}{y_o + Y_L} \tag{64}$$

This formula is valid whether or not the device is unilateral. It is also noted in Table 2-1 that the current gain

$$A_i = \frac{-z_f}{z_o + Z_L} \tag{65}$$

in terms of the z parameters and load impedance is similar in form to (64).

If the normalized load admittance is again defined to be

$$y = g + jb = \frac{G_L}{g_o} + j\frac{B_L + b_o}{g_o} \tag{66}$$

then (64) becomes

$$|A_v|^2 = \frac{|y_f/g_o|^2}{(g+1)^2 + b^2} = \frac{|A_{v_{max}}|^2}{(g+1)^2 + b^2} \tag{67}$$

where $|A_{v_{max}}| = |y_f/g_o|$ occurs when $g=0$ (i.e., $G_L = 0$) and $b=0$ (i.e., $B_L = -b_o$). Substituting for g and b from (61), performing the required manipulations and simplifying, (67) becomes

$$V^2 + (U-1)^2 = \left(\frac{2|A_v|}{|A_{v_{max}}|}\right)^2 \tag{68}$$

This represents a family of circles with centers at $V=0$ and $U=1$ on the Smith chart and with radii

$$r = \frac{2|A_v|}{|A_{v_{max}}|} \tag{69}$$

Several circles are drawn in Fig. 4-9 for different values of the voltage-gains ratio $|A_v|/|A_{v_{max}}|$. The Smith chart coordinates represent all possible normalized passive load admittances for any voltage gain $0 \leqslant |A_v| \leqslant |A_{v_{max}}|$.

It is noticed from (67), however, that

$$(g+1)^2 + b^2 = \frac{|A_{v_{max}}|^2}{|A_v|^2}$$

which represents a family of circles in the $g - jb$ plane. The centers are fixed at $g = -1$ and $b = 0$, but the radii vary from one to infinity for $0 \leqslant |A_v| \leqslant |A_{v_{max}}|$.

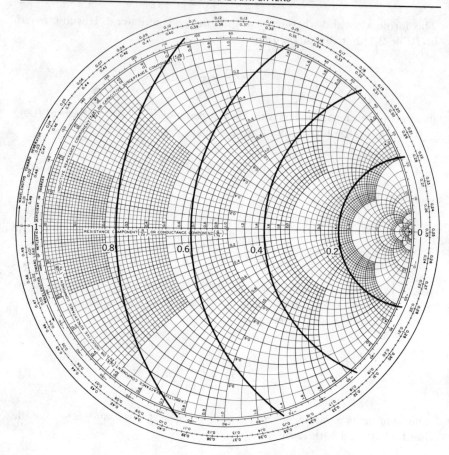

Figure 4-9. Voltage-gain circles for various values of $|Av|/|Av_{\max}|$.

The current gain of an amplifier is given in Table 2-1 as

$$A_i = \frac{y_f Y_L}{y_i y_o - y_r y_f + y_i Y_L}$$

It is convenient to rearrange this into the form

$$A_i = \frac{y_f/y_i}{Z_L(y_o - y_r y_f/y_i) + 1} \tag{70}$$

where $Z_L = 1/Y_L$. In the demoninator of (70), the load impedance is multiplied by an admittance factor; hence the product is dimensionless. That product can be considered to be the normalized load impedance

$$z_L = r + jx = Z_L \left(y_o - \frac{y_r y_f}{y_i} \right) \tag{71}$$

Then (70) becomes

$$A_i = \frac{y_f / y_i}{(r+1) + jx} \tag{72}$$

and

$$|A_i|^2 = \frac{|y_f / y_i|^2}{(r+1)^2 + x^2} \tag{73}$$

Equation (73) is the same form as (67) and leads to the family of circles given by

$$V^2 + (U-1)^2 = \left(\frac{2|A_i|}{|A_{i_{max}}|} \right)^2 \tag{74}$$

Since (74) is the same form as (68), the circles drawn in Fig. 4-9 can also be used to represent the current-gains ratios $|A_i| / |A_{i_{max}}|$. The main difference between the voltage-gain and current-gain cases is in the normalizing methods.

To simplify the situation to a unilateral case, let $y_r = 0$. Then (71) becomes

$$z_L = r + jx = z_L y_o \tag{75}$$

Since $Z_L = R_L + jX_L$ and $y_o = g_o + jb_o$, the normalized load values are

$$r = g_o R_L - b_o X_L \tag{76}$$

(of course, only $r > 0$ is useful on Smith chart) and

$$x = b_o R_L + g_o X_L \tag{77}$$

The inverse of the normalization process is obtained by solving (76) and (77) for

$$R_L = \frac{r g_o + x b_o}{g_o^2 + b_o^2} \tag{78}$$

and

$$X_L = \frac{x g_o - r b_o}{g_o^2 + b_o^2} \tag{79}$$

Maximum current gain is found from (72) or (73) for passive loads when $r=0$ and $x=0$. Thus (78) and (79) yield $R_L=0$ and $X_L=0$, or the actual load is a short circuit as expected. The maximum (short-circuit) current gain corresponds to the h_f parameter of Table 1-2, which is found there also to equal y_f/y_i.

The nonunilateral situation is conveniently handled by letting the admittance factor in the denominator of (70) be $\alpha+j\beta$. Then replace g_o by α and b_o by β in the normalizing expressions.

PROBLEMS

4-1. A unilateralized transistor has the following parameters at 10.7 MHz:

$$y_{11}=(0.7+j0.5)10^{-3} \qquad y_{12}=0.002\times10^{-3}\cong0$$

$$y_{21}=(-31.0+j11.3)10^{-3} \qquad y_{22}=(0.03+j0.6)10^{-3}$$

Determine (a) if the transistor is inherently stable. Why? (b) Maximum power gain. (c) Inherent bandwidths. (d) Optimum terminations. (e) Input and output capacitances.

4-2. In Problem 2-3, an additional capacitive susceptance of 0.117 mho (due to $C_L=310\,\text{pF}$) was required for an output circuit bandwidth of 2 MHz. The optimum load conductance was 2×10^{-3} mho. The matching network shown in Fig. 4-10 is to be used to transform the 50-Ω load into $Y_{\text{in}}=(2+j117)10^{-3}$ in order to provide the proper C_L and load conductance. Then an inductive susceptance is connected across terminals $A-B$ to resonate the total capacitive susceptance at 60 MHz.

(a) Use the series-parallel transformations of Section 4-22 to calculate C_1 and C_2. (b) Use the Smith Chart to check the results of (a).

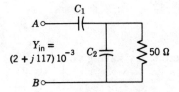

Figure 4-10.   Circuit for Problem 4-2.

4-3. Rewrite all relationships in Section 4-4 for the output circuit.

4-4. Two transistors identical to the one in Problem 4-1 are used in cascade at 10.7 MHz between 50-Ω terminations. (a) If no matching networks are used anywhere, calculate the overall power gain from the input terminals of the first transistor to the 50-Ω load of the second. (b) A matching network is used only between the signal source and first transistor. Is the power gain of (a) changed? (c) The second transistor is matched to the first and also to its own 50-Ω load. What is the overall power gain?

4-5.   A 10.7 MHz amplifier uses the transistor of Problem 4-1. The overall bandwidth is to be 250 kHz and the input and output circuits are to have identical bandwidths. Determine: (a) Bandwidth of input and output circuits; (b) C_s and C_L (c) Optimum terminations for the specified bandwidth conditions. (d) Design an input network to match a source admittance of $(0.03 + j0.6)10^{-3}$ to the transistor. (e) Design an output network to match a load admittance of $(0.7 + j0.5)10^{-3}$ to the transistor. (f) Calculate the tunability factor.

CHAPTER FIVE

HIGH-FREQUENCY AMPLIFIER DESIGN

5-0 INTRODUCTION

Circuit design can be performed in many different ways. Complete and detailed calculations can be made before any laboratory construction begins. Or step-by-step measurements and calculations can be automated and controlled by computer. Sometimes it is best to adopt completely or modify only slightly a standardized and tested circuit. The designer often has the experience to design with the actual components by adjusting values until measurements satisfy specifications, and few if any calculations need to be made. Maybe the latest state-of-the-art technique is purloined from a strong competitor by some devious means. One or more expert consultants are often called in to provide the answers. In any event, the end result of a properly operating circuit is an objective to be sought.

The purpose of this chapter is to discuss some of the techniques associated with the design of high-frequency amplifiers.

5-1 POWER GAIN VS. LOAD ADMITTANCE ON THE SMITH CHART

The effect of load admittance on power gain can be conveniently represented on the Smith chart. The power gain is

$$G_p = \frac{|y_f|^2 G_L}{|y_o + Y_L|^2 \operatorname{Re}\left[y_i - y_r y_f/(y_o + Y_L)\right]} \tag{1}$$

Let the normalized load admittance be

$$y = g + jb = \frac{G_L}{g_o} + j\frac{B_L + b_o}{g_o} \tag{2}$$

in which the imaginary part of the parameter y_o is included in the imaginary part of y.

Let the Smith chart transformation be represented by

$$U + jV = \frac{y-1}{y+1} = \frac{g-1+jb}{g+1+jb} \tag{3}$$

whose components are given by

$$U = \frac{g^2 - 1 + b^2}{(g+1)^2 + b^2} \quad \text{and} \quad V = \frac{2b}{(g+1)^2 + b^2} \tag{4}$$

Since $(y_o + Y_L) = (g_o + G_L) + j(b_o + B_L)$ and $y_r y_f = P + jQ$, the power gain, after some manipulation, can be written as

$$G_p = \frac{|y_f|^2 g}{g_o g_i\left[(g+1)^2 + b^2\right] - P(g+1) - Qb} \tag{5}$$

It can be shown that (4) and (5) can be combined into the form

$$\left(U + \frac{PG_p}{|y_f|^2}\right)^2 + \left(V - \frac{QG_p}{|y_f|^2}\right)^2 = r^2 \tag{6}$$

where

$$r = \left(1 - 2G_p\frac{2g_o g_i - P}{|y_f|^2} + G_p^2\frac{|y_r|^2}{|y_f|^2}\right)^{1/2} \tag{7}$$

Equation 6 represents a family of circles in the $U - jV$ plane with centers at

$$U = -\frac{PG_p}{|y_f|^2} \quad \text{and} \quad V = \frac{QG_p}{|y_f|^2} \tag{8}$$

and whose radii are given by (7). Each circle is for a specified power gain less than the maximum.

One of the factors in the second term on the right side of (7) has a special interpretation. From 2-37, the power gain is

$$G_p = \frac{|y_f|^2(G_2 - g_o)}{g_i(G_2{}^2 + B_2{}^2) - PG_2 - QB_2} \tag{8a}$$

where $G_2 = g_o + G_L$ and $B_2 = b_o + B_L$.

By setting $B_L = -b_o$ and $G_L = g_o$, (8a) becomes

$$G_{oo} = \frac{|y_f|^2 g_o}{g_i(4g_o^2) - 2Pg_o} = \frac{|y_f|^2}{2(2g_o g_i - P)} \tag{8b}$$

This is the power gain obtained when Y_L is the conjugate of the parameter y_o, and it is the reciprocal of the factor in (7). The constant-power-gain circle for G_{oo} passes through the center of the Smith chart, as seen from (6) by setting $U = V = 0$.

The centers are on a straight line through the origin that makes an angle

$$\phi = \tan^{-1} \frac{Q}{-P} \tag{9}$$

with the positive U axis. The distance between the centers and the origin is

$$d = \frac{|y_r|}{|y_f|} G_p \tag{10}$$

Thus (7) can be rewritten as

$$r = \left(1 + d^2 - \frac{G_p}{G_{oo}}\right)^{1/2} \tag{11}$$

The circles can be plotted on the Smith chart using (9), (10), and (11). The values of g and b in (2), representing normalized load admittance, are denoted by the conductance and susceptance markings on the Smith chart. The angle ϕ is given by the markings for "angle of reflection coefficient in degrees," and the distance d is obtained from the linear radial scale. The U and jV axes are discarded. The Smith chart now represents all possible passive normalized load admittances.

The circle for $G_p = 0$ is centered at $U = 0$, $V = 0$, (i.e., the center of the Smith chart), and its radius is $r = 1$. This circle corresponds to the outer circumference of the Smith chart. If the transistor is inherently stable, the radius decreases as the power gain increases until at $G_p = (G_p)_{\max}$ the radius becomes zero. The distance of this point along the straight line from the origin is

$$d_{max} = \frac{|y_r|}{|y_f|}(G_p)_{max} \qquad (12)$$

The values of g and b at this point represent the optimum normalized load admittance. The actual optimum values of $(G_L)_{opt}$ and $(B_L)_{opt}$ are then calculated using (2). It is useful to mark the power gain circles in dB.

Example   5-1

The CE y parameters of a 2N3783 transistor at 200 MHz are

$$y_{ie} = (20+j13)10^{-3} \qquad y_{re} = (-0.015-j0.502)10^{-3}$$

$$y_{fe} = (41.5-j64)10^{-3} \qquad y_{oe} = (0.25+j1.9)10^{-3}$$

Draw several constant-gain circles and determine the optimum load admittance.

Solution

Since $C = 0.895$ the transistor is inherently stable and $(G_p)_{max}$ is finite and equal to 94.1 or 19.7 dB. The value of G_{oo} is 67.8 or 18.3 dB.

$$y_r y_f = P+jQ = (-32.7-j19.93)10^{-6} = 38.3 \times 10^{-6} \;\underline{/211.3°}$$

$$\phi = \tan^{-1}\frac{Q}{-P} = \tan^{-1}\frac{-19.93}{32.7} = -\tan^{-1}0.61 = -31.4°$$

$$d_{max} = \frac{|y_r|}{|y_f|}(G_p)_{max} = \frac{0.502}{76.2}(94.1) = 0.62$$

This distance is measured along the straight line from the origin (i.e., center of the Smith chart) toward the $-31.4°$ marking on the reflection coefficient angle scale, as shown in Fig. 5-1.

The coordinates of the point are read as $g = 1.89$ and $b = -2$. Thus, from (2),

$$(G_L)_{opt} = gg_o = 1.89\,(0.25 \times 10^{-3}) = 0.472 \times 10^{-3}$$

and

$$(B_L)_{opt} = bg_o - b_o = -2(0.25 \times 10^{-3}) - 1.9 \times 10^{-3} = -2.4 \times 10^{-3}$$

which compare favorably with Example 2-2.

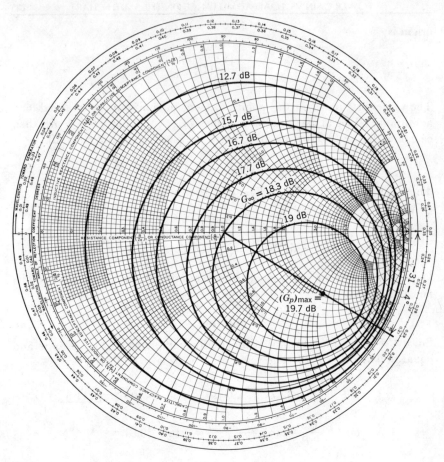

Figure 5-1.   Power-gain circles for Example 5-1.

**TABLE 5-1.   CALCULATED VALUES FOR
CONSTANT-POWER-GAIN CIRCLES FOR EXAMPLE 5-1**

dB	G_p Ratio	d	r
19.7	$94.1 = (G_p)_{\max}$	0.621	0
19.0	80	0.528	0.319
18.3	$68 = G_{oo}$	0.448	0.448
17.7	59	0.39	0.534
16.7	47	0.31	0.636
15.7	37.2	0.245	0.716
12.7	18.6	0.123	0.861

Table 5-1 gives the results of calculations for several power-gain circles, which are drawn as shown in Fig. 5-1. It is seen that a considerable variation in load admittance is possible without decreasing the power gain more than 3 dB.

A conjugate match should be provided at the input port to obtain maximum output power.

5-2 TUNABILITY

The tunability factor for the amplifier in Example 5-1 is $\delta \cong 0.656$ when the optimum load admittance is used. However, as discussed in Section 2-6, tunability is improved (i.e., δ is made smaller) by using a larger load admittance than the optimum value.

From 2-112, for $\delta = 0.3$,

$$G_L \cong \frac{|y_r y_f|}{0.3|y_i|} \tag{13}$$

Since normalized load admittances are represented by the Smith chart, divide (13) by g_o to obtain

$$g = \frac{G_L}{g_o} \cong \frac{|y_r y_f|}{0.3 g_o |y_i|} \tag{14}$$

Therefore specifying the tunability factor establishes a particular g circle on the Smith chart. Several power-gain circles cross this g circle, but the power-gain circle that is tangent to this g circle provides the most power gain. A reasonable, commonsense estimate may have to be made for the power gain at the point of tangency; however, the normalized load susceptance value b is the same as for the optimum load. Then, after calculating G_L and B_L using (2), the inequality $Y_L \gg y_o$ can be checked and the tunability factor recalculated using either 2-110 or 2-111.

Example 5-2

Determine the power gain and load admittance of the amplifier in Example 5-1 for a tunability factor of 0.3.

Solution

From (14),

$$g = \frac{38.3 \times 10^{-6}}{(0.3)(0.25 \times 10^{-3})(23.9 \times 10^{-3})} = 21.3$$

Unfortunately, the Smith chart is not highly detailed in this region, but it appears that a gain circle for only slightly more than 15.7 dB is tangent to the $g \cong 21.3$ circle. The power gain circles are tangent to the g circles on the b circle passing through $(B_L)_{\text{opt}}$. Therefore the normalized load susceptance is $b = -2$ as in Example 5-1.

Then

$$G_L = gg_o = 21.3(0.25 \times 10^{-3}) = 5.32 \times 10^{-3}$$

and

$$B_L = bg_o - b_o = (-2)(0.25 \times 10^{-3}) - 1.9 \times 10^{-3} = -2.4 \times 10^{-3}$$

Thus,

$$Y_L = G_L + jB_L = (5.32 - j2.4)10^{-3} = 5.84 \times 10^{-3} \quad \underline{/-24.3°}$$

To check the inequality $Y_L \gg y_o$, it is noticed that B_L and b_o are opposite in sign but almost the same magnitude, and that $G_L \gg g_o$. Therefore, the inequality is satisfied so that (2-111) applies.

$$\delta \cong \frac{|y_r y_f|}{|y_i||Y_L|} = \frac{38.3 \times 10^{-6}}{(23.9 \times 10^{-3})(5.84 \times 10^{-3})} = 0.274$$

This gives good tunability, with δ smaller than the original specification. Decreasing Y_L to $(5 - j2)10^{-3}$ makes $\delta \cong 0.3$ and increases the power gain slightly. For thus value of load admittance, the input admittance is calculated to be $(26.2 + j16.8)10^{-3}$.

5-3 INPUT ADMITTANCE ON THE SMITH CHART

Maximum operating power gain is determined by the optimum load admittance. A nonoptimum load produces less power gain but can improve tunability. Maximizing the output power with a nonoptimum load requires conjugate matching at the input port. Designing a matching network for the input port requires a knowledge of the input admittance. It is convenient to be able to determine input admittance graphically from the Smith chart for any choice of load admittance.

The input admittance is given by

$$Y_{\text{in}} = G_{\text{in}} + jB_{\text{in}} = y_i - \frac{y_r y_f}{y_o + Y_L} \tag{15}$$

Again, let

$$P + jQ = y_r y_f \tag{16}$$

$$y = g + jb = \frac{G_L}{g_o} + j\frac{B_L + b_o}{g_o} \tag{17}$$

$$U + jV = \frac{y - 1}{y + 1} \tag{18}$$

Using these four equations, it can be shown that

$$G_{in} = \left(\frac{P}{2g_o} \right) U - \left(\frac{Q}{2g_o} \right) V + \left(g_i - \frac{P}{2g_o} \right) \tag{19}$$

and

$$B_{in} = \left(\frac{Q}{2g_o} \right) U + \left(\frac{P}{2g_o} \right) V + \left(b_i - \frac{Q}{2g_o} \right) \tag{20}$$

Equations 19 and 20 represent a rectangular grid of constant-G_{in} lines and constant-B_{in} lines on the U-jV plane. Since the U-jV plane represents normalized load admittances on the Smith chart, constructing the rectangular grid on the Smith chart allows the input admittance to be read directly from the grid for any normalized load admittance.

The grid construction is simplified by noting that consecutive constant-G_{in} lines have a spacing along the U axis given by

$$\Delta U = \left(\frac{2g_o}{P} \right) \Delta G_{in} \tag{21}$$

where ΔG_{in} represents some arbitrary increment in the marking of the constant-G_{in} lines of the grid. Similarly, consecutive constant-B_{in} lines have a spacing along the V axis given by

$$\Delta V = \left(\frac{2g_o}{P} \right) \Delta B_{in} \tag{22}$$

where ΔB_{in} represents the increment in B_{in}. By choosing $\Delta G_{in} = \Delta B_{in} = 10$ mmho, for example, the grid intercepts along the U and jV axes will have identical spacings as given by (21) or (22). Additional lines of the grid can be constructed as needed to make ΔG_{in} and/or ΔB_{in} smaller.

From (20), the constant-B_{in} lines make an angle with the positive U axis given by

$$\tan^{-1} \left(\frac{dV}{dU} \right) = \tan^{-1} \frac{Q}{-P} \tag{23}$$

which is the same as the angle ϕ of (9) for the line along which the centers of the constant-power gain circles are located.

In order to properly position the grid on the Smith chart at least one point must be calculated to determine G_{in} and B_{in}. This may be done using (19) and (20) and calculating G_{in} and B_{in} at the center of the Smith chart where $U = V = 0$.

Example 5-3

Construct on a Smith chart the input admittance grid for the amplifier of Examples 5-1 and 5-2.

Solution

If $\Delta G_{in} = \Delta B_{in} = 10 \times 10^{-3}$, then

$$\Delta U = \Delta V = \left(\frac{2g_o}{P}\right)\Delta G_{in} = \frac{2(0.25 \times 10^{-3})(10 \times 10^{-3})}{-32.7 \times 10^{-6}} = -0.153$$

The minus sign means that U and V decrease by 0.153 as G_{in} and B_{in} increase by 10×10^{-3}. About 16 parallel lines per set cover the entire Smith chart with this spacing, but the grid need not be drawn anywhere except in the region of particular interest.

To position the grid, let $U = V = 0$. Then

$$G_{in}\big|_{U=V=0} = \left(g_i - \frac{P}{2g_o}\right) = 20 \times 10^{-3} + \frac{32.7 \times 10^{-6}}{0.5 \times 10^{-3}} = 85.4 \times 10^{-3}$$

and

$$B_{in}\big|_{U=V=0} = \left(b_i - \frac{Q}{2g_o}\right) = 13 \times 10^{-3} - \frac{-19.93 \times 10^{-6}}{0.5 \times 10^{-3}} = 52.9 \times 10^{-3}$$

The constant-B_{in} lines are at an angle $-31.4°$ with respect to the positive U axis. The grid is constructed as shown in Fig. 5-2.

For example 5-1, with $g = 1.89$ and $b = -2$, the input admittance is read from the grid as

$$Y_{in} \cong (38 + j53)10^{-3}$$

For example 5-2, with $g = 21.3$ and $b = -2.0$, the input admittance is read as

$$Y_{in} \cong (26 + j17)10^{-3}$$

Considerable time and effort is expended in positioning and constructing the grid, and it may be questionable to do this if the input admittance at only one or two points is desired. However, the constant power-gain circles of Fig. 5-1 and the input admittance grid of Fig. 5-2 are a powerful design combination for picturing the influence of load admittance. Observe also that no value of load admittance causes negative input conductance for the case shown in Fig. 5-2.

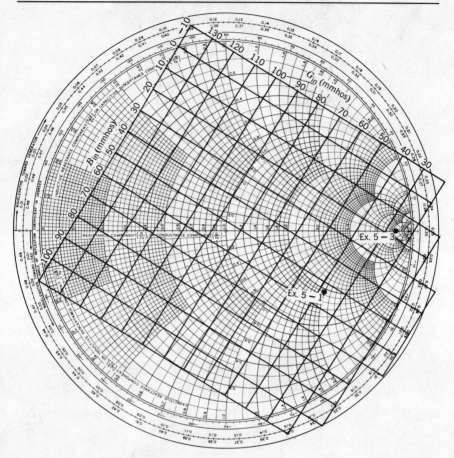

Figure 5-2.   Input admittance grid for Example 5-3.

5-31 The line for $G_{in} = 0$

If the line for $G_{in} = 0$ falls inside the load-admittance Smith chart, there exist load admittances for which G_{in} is negative. This line also represents zero input power (i.e., it allows no input conductive current, hence, no power) and infinite power gain. Therefore the distance of this line from the origin of the U-jV plane (i.e., the center of the Smith chart) is important.

Consider the construction shown in Fig. 5-3. Distance X between the chart center and the $G_{in} = 0$ line is measured along one of the constant-B_{in} lines that are at angle ϕ given by (23). Then $\tan\phi = Q/(-P)$, so that

$$\sin\phi = \frac{Q}{\sqrt{P^2 + Q^2}} \tag{24}$$

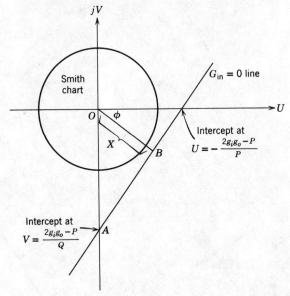

Figure 5-3. *Construction showing the line for* $G_{in} = 0$ *located distance X from the center of the Smith chart.*

From (19), the equation for the $G_{in} = 0$ line is

$$\left(\frac{P}{2g_o}\right)U - \left(\frac{Q}{2g_o}\right)V + \left(g_i - \frac{P}{2g_o}\right) = 0 \tag{25}$$

The line has an intercept on the jV axis given by setting $U = 0$ in (25) and solving for V to obtain

$$V_{intercept} = \frac{2g_o g_i - P}{Q} \tag{26}$$

Since angle OAB equals ϕ, the sine of this angle is

$$\sin\phi = \frac{X}{(2g_o g_i - P)/Q} = \frac{XQ}{2g_o g_i - P} \tag{27}$$

Equate (24) and (27) to obtain

$$X = \frac{2g_i g_o - P}{\sqrt{P^2 + Q^2}} \tag{28}$$

But since this is exactly the reciprocal of the stability factor C,

$$X = \frac{1}{C} \tag{29}$$

If the transistor is inherently stable, $C < 1$, so $X > 1$. If the transistor is potentially unstable, $C > 1$, so $X < 1$. In Fig. 5-2, $X = 1/0.895 = 1.12$.

When $0 < X < 1$, that section of the Smith chart that extends from the $G_{in} = 0$ line toward and beyond the center of the Smith chart represents the stable region. The section of the Smith chart on the other side of this $G_{in} = 0$ line represents the unstable region.

When $-1 < X < 0$, the $G_{in} = 0$ line is drawn at a distance $+X$ along the line whose angle is $\phi \pm 180°$. In this case, the section of the Smith chart that extends from the $G_{in} = 0$ line toward and beyond the center of the Smith chart represents the unstable region. The section of the Smith chart on the other side of this $G_{in} = 0$ line represents the stable region.

When $X < -1$, the $G_{in} = 0$ line is outside the Smith chart. This means that there is no passive load that can make the input conductance positive.

Knowing the location of the $G_{in} = 0$ line and the value of G_{in} for $U = V = 0$, the scale for other G_{in} lines can be established as an aid in drawing all G_{in} lines.

The $B_{in} = 0$ line can be located in similar fashion at a distance

$$\frac{Q - 2g_o b_i}{\sqrt{P^2 + Q^2}} \tag{30}$$

from the center of the Smith chart. If the $B_{in} = 0$ line falls inside the Smith chart, there will exist certain load admittances for which the input admittance is pure conductance.

5-32 Normalized Input Admittance

The time and effort required for positioning and constructing the grid for actual input admittance can be reduced by using a pair of axes for normalized input admittance. The development of the normalized axes may begin by rewriting (19) and (20) as

$$2g_o(G_{in} - g_i) + P = PU - QV \tag{31}$$

and

$$2g_o(B_{in} - b_i) + Q = QU + PV \tag{32}$$

However, since

$$(P + jQ)(U + jV) = (PU - QV) + j(QU + PV) \tag{33}$$

then (31) and (32) can be combined as

$$[2g_o(G_{in}-g_i)+P]+j[2g_o(B_{in}-b_i)+Q]=(P+jQ)(U+jV) \qquad (34)$$

But

$$P+jQ=\sqrt{P^2+Q^2} \quad \underline{/\theta}$$

where

$$\theta=\tan^{-1}\frac{Q}{P}$$

Therefore (34) becomes

$$\left[\frac{2g_o(G_{in}-g_i)+P}{\sqrt{P^2+Q^2}}+j\frac{2g_o(B_{in}-b_i)+Q}{\sqrt{P^2+Q^2}}\right] \underline{/-\theta}=U+jV \qquad (35)$$

Now, by defining the normalized conductance and susceptance values as

$$G'_{in}=\frac{2g_o(G_{in}-g_i)+P}{\sqrt{P^2+Q^2}} \qquad (36)$$

and

$$B'_{in}=\frac{2g_o(B_{in}-b_i)+Q}{\sqrt{P^2+Q^2}} \qquad (37)$$

(35) becomes

$$(G'_{in}+jB'_{in}) \quad \underline{/-\theta}=U+jV \qquad (38)$$

The normalized components G'_{in} and jB'_{in} represent rectangular coordinate axes whose values vary linearly from -1 to $+1$ in the same way as for the U and jV axes of the Smith chart.

The construction required by (38) is simply to rotate the normalized axes through the angle $-\theta$, draw the two perpendicular axes through the center of the Smith chart, and label the axes including the appropriate signs. Then the values of G'_{in} and B'_{in} may be found for any point on the Smith chart by noting the distances between the point and each normalized axis using a compass or dividers, transferring the distances to the linear radial scale from which numerical values for the normalized components are obtained, and then providing the proper signs.

Example 5-4

Determine the input admittance for the amplifier of Examples 5-1 and 5-2.

Solution

The rotation angle is $-211.3°$. The axes are drawn and labeled in Figure 5-4. For Example 5-1, the normalized values are found to be $G'_{in} = -0.622$ and $B'_{in} = 0$. Then from (36) and (37), the actual conductance and susceptance values are

$$G_{in} = G'_{in} \frac{\sqrt{P^2 + Q^2}}{2g_o} + \left(g_i - \frac{P}{2g_o} \right)$$

$$= 37.8 \times 10^{-3} \text{ mho} \qquad (39)$$

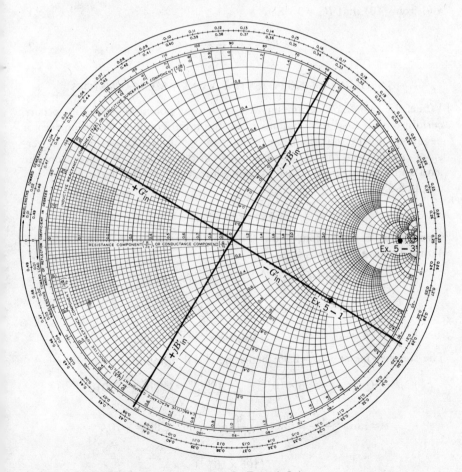

Figure 5-4. Normalized input admittance axes for Example 5-4.

and

$$B_{in} = B'_{in} \frac{\sqrt{P^2 + Q^2}}{2g_o} + \left(b_i - \frac{Q}{2g_o}\right)$$

$$= 52.9 \times 10^{-3} \text{ mho} \tag{40}$$

For Example 5-2, the normalized values are found to be $G'_{in} = -0.781$ and $B'_{in} = -0.47$. Then $G_{in} = 25.6 \times 10^{-3}$ mho and $B_{in} = 16.6 \times 10^{-3}$ mho.

It is also noticed from (39) that $G_{in} \geqslant 0$ when

$$G'_{in} \geqslant \frac{P - 2g_i g_o}{\sqrt{P^2 + Q^2}} \tag{41}$$

and from (40) that $B_{in} = 0$ when

$$B'_{in} = \frac{Q - 2b_i g_o}{\sqrt{P^2 + Q^2}} \tag{42}$$

5-4 DESIGN USING POTENTIALLY UNSTABLE TRANSISTORS

When the transistor parameters are such that potential instability occurs, certain output load terminations cause the input conductance to be zero or negative and the maximum power gain to be infinite. However, the power-gain circles and the input-admittance grid can still be drawn on the load-admittance Smith chart. A procedure to follow is illustrated by Example 5-5.

Example 5-5

Investigate the operation of the 2N3783 transistor at 60 MHz when the parameters are

$$y_{ie} = (5 + j4)10^{-3} \qquad y_{re} = (0 - j0.3)10^{-3}$$

$$y_{fe} = (100 - j35)10^{-3} \qquad y_{oe} = (0.3 + j1)10^{-3}$$

Solution

The stability factor is $C = 2.35$; hence potential instability is established.

$$P + jQ = y_r y_f = 31.8 \times 10^{-6} \underline{/-109.3°} = (-10.5 - j30)10^{-6}$$

$$\phi = \tan^{-1} \frac{Q}{-P} = \tan^{-1} \frac{-30}{10.5} = -\tan^{-1} 2.86 = -70.7°$$

$$G_{oo} = \frac{|y_f|^2}{2(2g_i g_o - P)} = \frac{(106 \times 10^{-3})^2}{2[2(5)(0.3) + 10.5]10^{-6}} = 417 = 26.2 \text{ dB}$$

Table 5-2 gives the results of calculations for several power gain circles shown in Fig. 5-5. To assure stability, it is seen that $g \geqslant 6.1$ keeps load admittance in the stable region.

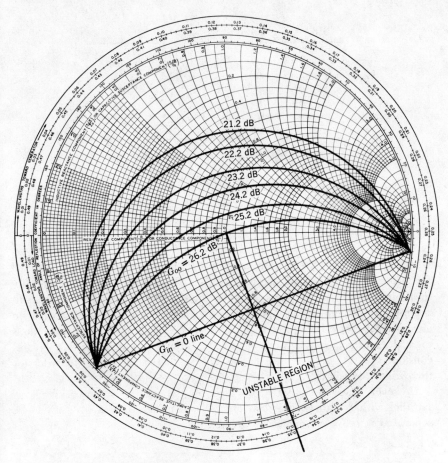

Figure 5-5.   Power gain circles for Examples 5-5.

For good tunability, normalized load conductance is

$$g = \frac{G_L}{g_o} \cong \frac{|y_r y_f|}{0.3|y_i|g_o} = \frac{31.8 \times 10^{-6}}{0.3(6.4)(0.3)10^{-6}} = 55.2$$

There is insufficient detail in this part of the Smith chart to obtain worthwhile readings.

TABLE 5-2 CALCULATED VALUES FOR
CONSTANT-POWER-GAIN CIRCLES FOR EXAMPLE 5-5

dB	G_p Ratio	d	r
26.2	$417 = G_{oo}$	1.18	1.18
25.2	330	0.933	1.03
24.2	262	0.742	0.96
23.2	210	0.594	0.92
22.2	165	0.467	0.912

5-41 A Mismatching Technique

It was shown in Section 2.2 that when

$$g_i g_o > \frac{P+M}{2} \tag{43}$$

where $P + jQ = M \underline{/\theta} = y_r y_f$, the transistor itself is inherently stable. Thus, if the product $g_i g_o$ is not sufficient to satisfy (43), the transistor is potentially unstable. Even if the product $g_i g_o$ is too small for inherent stability, it is still possible to do something about the choice of terminations in order to effectively increase the product $g_i g_o$. Of course, one thing that can be done is to add external conductance across the input or output terminals and consider the external conductance as having increased g_i or g_o in order for the *circuit* to satisfy (43).

However, since G_s and G_L provided by the matching networks are in parallel with g_i and g_o, it is convenient to consider G_s and G_L each to be separated into two conductances defined by

$$G_s = G_S' + G_S'' \tag{44}$$

and

$$G_L = G_L' + G_L'' \tag{45}$$

Now let G_L'' and G_S'' be added to g_i and g_o, respectively, to obtain the new parameter conductances

$$g_i' = g_i + G_S'' \tag{46}$$

and

$$g_o' = g_o + G_L'' \tag{47}$$

Then, the *circuit* will be stable if, at least,

$$g_i' g_o' = (g_i + G_S'')(g_o + G_L'') > \frac{P + M}{2} \tag{48}$$

even though the transistor itself is potentially unstable.

A measure of the amount of inequality in (48) and, therefore, a measure of the least degree of stability may be defined as

$$K' = \frac{2(g_i + G_S'')(g_o + G_L'')}{P + M} = \frac{2 g_i g_o (1 + G_S''/g_i)(1 + G_L''/g_o)}{P + M} \tag{49}$$

Of course the total conductances are $(g_i + G_s)$ and $(g_o + G_L)$ so that the overall circuit stability is measured by

$$K = \frac{2(g_i + G_s)(g_o + G_L)}{P + M} = \frac{2 g_i g_o (1 + G_s/g_i)(1 + G_L/g_o)}{P + M} \tag{50}$$

Thus, K will be larger than K' for passive terminations because $G_s > G_S''$ and $G_L > G_L''$. The circuit is stable if $K > 1$ and unstable if $K < 1$. The ratios G_s/g_i and G_L/g_o are called mismatch ratios.

Now if K' is selected to be equal to or larger than $+1$, and if the transistor parameters are increased (i.e., augmented) to $Y_i' = g_i' + jb_i = (g_i + G_S'') + jb_i$, and $y_o' = g_o' + jb_o = (g_o + G_L'') + jb_o$, then the augmented transistor is conditionally stable or inherently stable. This means that the Smith chart procedures discussed in Section 5-1 can be used.

First, G_S'' and G_L'' must be determined. From (49)

$$(1 + G_S''/g_i)(1 + G_L''/g_o) = \frac{K'(P + M)}{2 g_i g_o} \tag{51}$$

There are many possible choices for the mismatch ratios in (51) for a given K'. For example, three choices are

(A) G_S''/g_i can be chosen equal to zero, and G_L''/g_o calculated to satisfy (51), or

(B) G_L''/g_o can be chosen equal to zero and G_S''/g_i calculated to satisfy (51), or

(C) the mismatch ratios can be chosen to be equal. For choice C, (51) becomes

$$(1 + G_S''/g_i)^2 = (1 + G_L''/g_o)^2 = \frac{K'(P + M)}{2 g_i g_o} \tag{52}$$

which yields

$$\frac{G_S''}{g_i} = \frac{G_L''}{g_o} = \sqrt{\frac{K'(P+M)}{2g_ig_o} - 1} \tag{53}$$

To simplify power-gain calculations, to help provide good tunability by using a large load admittance, and to allow the use of the Smith chart, choice A is convenient although not necessarily the best. Choice A leads to the circuit shown in Fig. 5.6 in which y_i remains unchanged because $G_S'' = 0$.

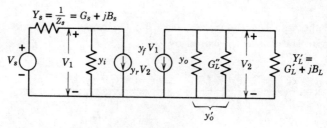

Figure 5-6.   The circuit for Choice A.

The operating power gain for the augmented transistor with load $Y_L' = G_L' + jB_L$ is, from (1),

$$G_p' = \frac{|y_f|^2 G_L'}{|y_o' + Y_L'|^2 \mathrm{Re}\left[y_i - \dfrac{y_r y_f}{y_o' + Y_L'}\right]} \tag{54}$$

Let the normalized load admittance be

$$y' = g' + jb' = \frac{G_L'}{g_o'} + j\frac{B_L + b_o}{g_o'} \tag{55}$$

and let the Smith chart transformation be

$$U + jV = \frac{y'-1}{y'+1} = \frac{g'-1+jb'}{g'+1+jb'} \tag{56}$$

Then (54) becomes

$$G_p' = \frac{|y_f|^2 g'}{g_ig_o'\left[(g'+1)^2 + b'^2\right] - P(g'+1) - Qb'} \tag{57}$$

Using

$$U = \frac{g'^2 - 1 + b'^2}{(g'+1)^2 + b'^2} \quad \text{and} \quad V = \frac{2b'}{(g'+1)^2 + b'^2}$$

from (56), it can be shown that (57) can be rearranged as

$$\left(U + \frac{PG_p'}{|y_f|^2} \right)^2 + \left(V - \frac{QG_p'}{|y_f|^2} \right)^2 = r'^2 \tag{58}$$

where

$$r' = \left(1 - 2G_p' \frac{2g_i g_o' - P}{|y_f|^2} + G_p'^2 \frac{|y_r|^2}{|y_f|^2} \right)^{1/2} \tag{59}$$

Equation (58) represents a family of circles whose centers are on a straight line through the origin at an angle

$$\phi = \tan^{-1} \frac{Q}{-P} \tag{60}$$

as before, and at a distance equal to

$$d' = \frac{|y_r|}{|y_f|} G_p' \tag{61}$$

Also,

$$G_{oo}' = \frac{|y_f|^2}{2(2g_i g_o' - P)} \tag{62}$$

When optimum termination are used, the maximum power gain of the augmented transistor is, from 2-42,

$$(G_p')_{\max} = \frac{|y_f|^2}{2g_i g_o' - P + \sqrt{(2g_i g_o' - P)^2 - M^2}} \tag{63}$$

Now specifically for choice A with $K' = 1.0$, $2g_i g_o' - P = M = |y_r y_f|$. Thus (63) becomes (for this choice and $K' = 1.0$ only),

$$(G_p')_{\max} = \frac{|y_f|^2}{|y_r||y_f|} = \frac{|y_f|}{|y_r|} \tag{64}$$

and (62) becomes

$$G'_{oo} = \frac{|y_f|^2}{2|y_r||y_f|} = \frac{|y_f|}{2|y_r|} = \frac{(G'_p)_{max}}{2} \tag{65}$$

Therefore (61) becomes

$$d' = \frac{G'_p}{(G'_p)_{max}} \tag{66}$$

Thus $d'_{max} = 1$ when $G'_p = (G'_p)_{max}$. Using (61) and (62) in (59), the radii become

$$r' = \sqrt{1 - \frac{G'_p}{G'_{oo}} + d'^2} \tag{67}$$

Then using (65) and (66) in (67),

$$r' = \sqrt{1 - 2d' + d'^2} = 1 - d' \tag{68}$$

Observe that $d' + r' = d' + 1 - d' = 1$. This means that calculations for constructing the circles are simplified considerably by using (66) and (68), when choice A with $K' = 1$ is considered. Also, $r' = 0$ when $d' = d'_{max} = 1$ for $G'_p = (G'_p)_{max}$.

Since G''_L is produced by the matching network rather than by a fixed conductance connected across the output terminals, the total useful output power is the sum of the powers delivered to both G'_L and G''_L. Therefore the actual power gain is

$$G_p = G'_p \frac{G'_L + G''_L}{G'_L} = G'_p \frac{G_L}{G'_L} \tag{69}$$

when the circuit is stable.

If it is assumed that $|Y_L| = G_L$, then from (2-111), the tunability factor varies inversely as G_L. Thus

$$\delta = \frac{|y_r y_f|}{|y_i| G_L} \tag{70}$$

is the tunability factor for the actual amplifier, and

$$\delta' = \frac{|y_r y_f|}{|y_i| G'_L} \tag{71}$$

is the tunability factor of the augmented transistor whose load conductance is G'_L. Combining (70) and (71) yields

$$\delta = \delta' \frac{G'_L}{G_L} \tag{72}$$

Since $G'_L < G_L$, then $\delta < \delta'$. Thus, if the augmented transistor amplifier is designed for $\delta' \leqslant 0.3$, then the actual amplifier is assured of having a satisfactory tunability factor.

One of the major benefits of this mismatching technique is that the region of the Smith chart in Fig. 5-5 where $g \geqslant 6.1$ has been expanded effectively into the entire Smith chart of Fig. 5-7 for $g' \geqslant 0$.

Example   5-6

The CE parameters of the potentially unstable transistor in Example 5-5 are

$$y_{ie} = (5+j4)10^{-3} \qquad y_{re} = (-j0.3)10^{-3}$$

$$y_{fe} = (100-j35)10^{-3} \qquad y_{oe} = (0.3+j1)10^{-3}$$

Using Choice A for the mismatch ratios in (51) with $K' = 1.0$, determine:
(a) $G''_L \cdot y'_{oe}$, G'_{oo}, and $(G'_p)_{max}$.
(b) Construction of several power-gain circles for G'_p.
(c) Y'_L, which makes the tunability factor of the augmented transistor equal to 0.3 and provides the highest possible power gain G'_p.
(d) Y_L, from the condition in (c), the associated power gain G_p, and the tunability factor δ.

Solution

$$P+jQ = y_{re}y_{fe} = (-10.5-j30)10^{-6} = 31.8 \times 10^{-6} \quad \underline{/-109.3°}$$

$$\phi = \tan^{-1}\frac{Q}{-P} = \tan^{-1}\frac{-30}{10.5} = -70.7°$$

(a) Using Choice A with $K' = 1.0$ and $G''_S = 0$ in (51) yields

$$\frac{G''_L}{g_o} = \frac{K'(P+M)}{2g_ig_o} - 1 = \frac{1.0(-10.5+31.8)10^{-6}}{2\times5\times0.3\times10^{-6}} - 1 = 6.1 \tag{73}$$

Note that this checks with Fig. 5-5 as the least value of g above which stability is assured. Then, from (73),

$$G''_L = 6.1g_o = 6.1 \times 0.3 \times 10^{-3} = 1.83 \times 10^{-3} \text{ mho} \tag{74}$$

Then,

$$y'_{oe} = (g_o + G''_L) + jb_o = [(0.3 + 1.83) + j1]10^{-3} = (2.13 + j1)10^{-3} \quad (75)$$

Thus $g'_{oe} = 2.13 \times 10^{-3}$ mho.

The Linvill stability factor for the augmented transistor is

$$C' = \frac{M}{2g_i g'_o - P} = \frac{M}{M} = 1.0$$

as expected when $K' = 1.0$. Also, from (64),

$$(G'_p)_{max} = \frac{|y_f|}{|y_r|} = 354 = 25.5 \text{ dB}$$

and from (65),

$$G'_{oo} = \frac{(G'_p)_{max}}{2} = 177 = 22.5 \text{ dB}$$

(b) Table 5-3 gives the results of calculations for the several power-gain circles that are shown in Fig. 5-7. The Smith chart coordinates are as specified in (55). So $g' = G'_L / g'_o$ and G'_L represents any load conductance in addition to the amount $G''_L = 1.83 \times 10^{-3}$ mho required to make $K' = 1.0$. Thus for any $G'_L > 0$, $K > 1$ and the circuit is stable.

TABLE 5-3   CALCULATED VALUES FOR
CONSTANT-POWER-GAIN CIRCLES WITH $K' = 1.0$
IN EXAMPLE 5-6

dB	G'_p Ratio	d	r
25.5	$354 = G'_{p(max)}$	1.00	0
24.5	282	0.797	0.203
23.5	224	0.634	0.366
22.5	$177 = G'_{oo}$	0.50	0.50
20.5	112	0.316	0.684

(c) For $\delta' = 0.3$,

$$g' = \frac{G'_L}{g'_o} = \frac{|y_r y_f|}{\delta' g'_o |y_i|} = \frac{31.8}{0.3 \times 2.13 \times 6.4} = 7.8 \quad (76)$$

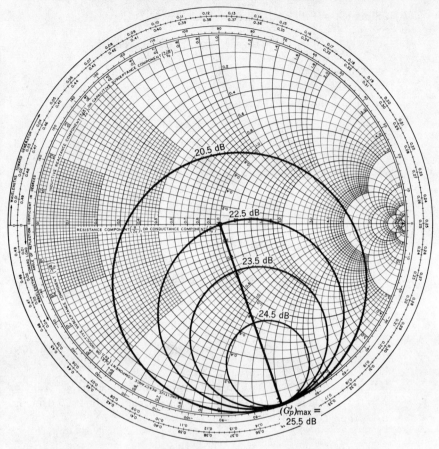

Figure 5-7.   Power-gain circles for Example 5-6.

It appears that a power-gain circle for about 20 dB is tangent to $g' = 7.8$ in Fig. 5-7. At this point, $b' = -1.41$ [the same b' circle that passes through $(G'_p)_{max}$]. Then

$$G'_L = g'g'_o = 7.8 \times 2.13 \times 10^{-3} = 16.6 \times 10^{-3}$$

and

$$B_L = b'g'_o - b_o = (-1.41 \times 2.13 - 1)10^{-3} = -4 \times 10^{-3}$$

so

$$Y'_L = G'_L + jB_L = (16.6 - j4)10^{-3} \tag{77}$$

(d) Since $G_L'' = 1.83 \times 10^{-3}$ from (74), then

$$Y_L = (G_L' + G_L'') + jB_L = [(16.6 + 1.83) - j4]10^{-3}$$

$$= (18.43 - j4)10^{-3}$$

From (5), the power gain is

$$G_p = \frac{|y_f|^2 g}{g_i g_o\left[(g+1)^2 + b^2\right] - P(g+1) - Qb} \qquad (78)$$

where

$$g = \frac{G_L}{g_o} = \frac{18.43}{0.3} = 61.5$$

and

$$b = \frac{B_L + b_o}{g_o} = \frac{-4+1}{0.3} = \frac{-3}{0.3} = -10$$

Substituting values into (78) gives

$$G_p = 109 = 20.37 \text{ dB} \qquad (79)$$

There is another way to find this power gain. Since the $g' = 7.8$ (for $\delta' = 0.3$) circle is tangent to a power-gain circle for about 20 dB (Fig. 5-7), then $G_p' \cong 100$. Then, using (69),

$$G_p = G_p' \times \frac{G_L}{G_L'} \cong \frac{100 \times 18.43}{16.6} = 111 \qquad (80)$$

which is essentially the same as in (79).

From (72), the tunability factor is

$$\delta = \delta' \frac{G_L'}{G_L} = \frac{0.3 \times 16.6}{18.43} = 0.27 \qquad (81)$$

which assumes $|Y_L| = G_L$. Using (2-111),

$$\delta = \frac{|y_r y_f|}{|y_i||Y_L|} = \frac{31.8}{6.4 \times 18.85} = 0.264 \qquad (82)$$

5-42 An Instability Caused by the Emitter Circuit

A typical amplifier circuit is shown in Fig. 5-8a. Resistances R_1, R_2, and R_E establish the desired DC operating point and its stability against temperature changes and transistor parameter variations. The emitter capacitance C_E is often selected to make its reactance at the lowest frequency of operation about one-tenth of R_E. (Of course, if $R_C = 0$ and the output is taken across R_E, an emitter follower is obtained.)

At this point, the circuit designer is prone to neglect the emitter-circuit impedance when calculating input and output impedances, amplifier gains, etc. Then after carefully constructing and testing the circuit, he finds that measured values do not always agree with the values the calculations indicated, and often an instability in the form of high-frequency oscillation may be encountered. This state of affairs can produce disturbing perplexity, particularly if the transistor itself is inherently stable.

Some insight into this situation may be obtained by examining the overall y parameters for the transistor and $R_E - C_E$ combination in Fig. 5-8b. Let these overall parameters be y_{11}, y_{12}, y_{21}, and y_{22}. From straightforward circuit analysis, it is found that

$$y_{11} = y_i - \frac{(y_i + y_f)(y_i + y_r)}{(y_i + y_r + y_f + y_o) + Y_E} \tag{83}$$

$$y_{12} = y_r - \frac{(y_i + y_r)(y_o + y_r)}{(y_i + y_r + y_f + y_o) + Y_E} \tag{84}$$

$$y_{21} = y_f - \frac{(y_i + y_f)(y_o + y_f)}{(y_i + y_r + y_f + y_o) + Y_E} \tag{85}$$

$$y_{22} = y_o - \frac{(y_o + y_f)(y_o + y_r)}{(y_i + y_r + y_f + y_o) + Y_E} \tag{86}$$

where $Y_E = (1/R_E) + j\omega C_E = G_E + jB_E$. The form of all these expressions is similar to the form of (15) for input admittance, provided the quantities within parentheses are given appropriate interpretations. Therefore the Smith chart can be used to show how the normalized admittance of the $R_E - C_E$ parallel combination influences each of the parameters.

If (83) is considered, a question arises about whether there is some value of Y_E for which $\mathrm{Re}\, y_{11} = g_{11}$ becomes negative. If so, the circuit is potentially unstable. Examples illustrate the procedures.

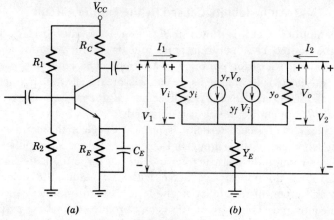

Figure 5-8. (a) Typical transistor amplifier. (b) Equivalent circuit for the transistor and R_E-C_E combination.

Example 5-7

The transistor in Fig. 5-8a has the following CE parameters:

$$y_i = (2.5 + j2.3)10^{-3} \qquad y_r = \text{negligible}$$

$$y_f = (10 - j19)10^{-3} \qquad y_o = (0.01 + j0.8)10^{-3}$$

Determine the influence of Y_E on y_{11}.

Solution

Since y_r is negligible, $g_i > 0$, and $g_o > 0$, the transistor itself is inherently stable. Also, from (83),

$$y_{11} = g_{11} + jb_{11} = y_i - \frac{(y_i + y_f)y_i}{(y_i + y_f + y_o) + Y_E} \qquad (87)$$

Now let

$$P' + jQ' = M' \underline{/\theta'} = (y_i + y_f)y_i$$

$$= (69.6 - j13)10^{-6}$$

$$= 70.8 \times 10^{-6} \quad \underline{/-10.58°} \qquad (88)$$

and

$$y_o' = g_o' + jb_o' = (y_i + y_f + y_o)$$

$$= (12.51 - j15.9)10^{-3}$$

To determine if some value of Y_E can cause g_{11} to become negative, it is necessary to use the stability criteria. Thus $g_i > 0$ $g_o' > 0$, and

$$C = \frac{M'}{2g_i g_o' - P'} = -10.1 \tag{89}$$

Since $C < 0$, there is some value of Y_E for which $g_{11} < 0$ as determined from the location of a $g_{11} = 0$ line on the Smith chart. Construct the $g_{11} = 0$ line using the U and jV axis intercepts given by

$$U_{\text{intercept}} = -\frac{2g_i g_o' - P'}{P'} = 0.101 \tag{90}$$

$$V_{\text{intercept}} = \frac{2g_i g_o' - P'}{Q'} = 0.542 \tag{91}$$

Locate the intercepts using the linear radial scale and draw the $g_{11} = 0$ line as shown in Fig. 5-9. Check its location relative to the angle

$$\phi = \tan^{-1} \frac{Q'}{-P'} = \tan^{-1} \frac{-13}{-69.7} = 180° + 10.58° \tag{92}$$

Calculate distance X and determine the region for which $g_{11} > 0$ and for which $g_{11} < 0$. Thus,

$$X = \frac{1}{C} = -0.099 \tag{93}$$

Since $-1 < X < 0$, the $g_{11} = 0$ line can be drawn at a distance $+0.099$ along a line through the center of the chart and whose angle is $+10.58°$. Now that section of the Smith chart that extends from the $g_{11} = 0$ line toward and beyond the center of the chart represents the region where $g_{11} < 0$.

The Smith chart coordinates are given by the normalized admittance of the $R_E - C_E$ combination, or

$$y_E = g_E + jb_E = \frac{G_E}{g_o'} + j\frac{B_E + b_o'}{g_o'} \tag{94}$$

where $G_E = 1/R_E$ and $B_E = \omega C_E$.

It is noted in Fig. 5-9 that a circle for $g_E \cong 1.24$ is tangent to the $g_{11} = 0$ line, at which point $b_E \cong -0.2$. To assure that g_{11} never becomes negative regardless of the value of C_E, g_E should not be less than 1.24. This condition

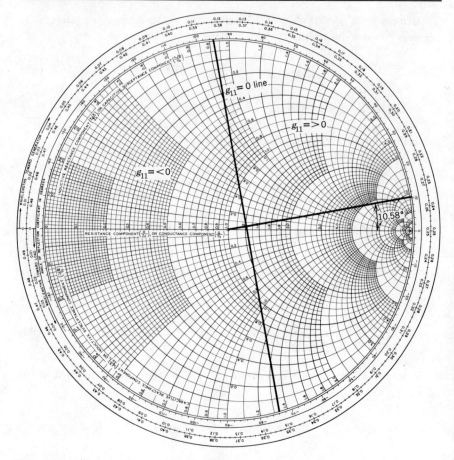

Figure 5-9. Location of the $g_{11} = 0$ line for Example 5-7.

means that

$$R_E < \frac{1}{1.24 g_o'} = \frac{1}{1.24(12.51)10^{-3}} = 64.5 \ \Omega$$

When $R_E > 64.5 \ \Omega$, the circle for $g_E < 1.24$ crosses the $g_{11} = 0$ line at two points. If, for example, $g_E = 0.5$, the two points of crossing are at $b_E = -1.27$ and $+0.85$. From (94),

$$C_E = \frac{b_E g_o' - b_o'}{\omega} \tag{95}$$

To assure that $g_{11} > 0$, $b_E < -1.27$ or $b_E > 0.85$. But $C_E = 0$ for $b_E = -1.27$ and C_E becomes negative for $b_E < -1.27$. However, $C_E = 26.5 \times 10^{-3}/\omega$ for $b_E = +0.85$. Thus g_{11} will be positive if $C_E > 26.5 \times 10^{-3}/\omega$.

Example 5-8

Determine the influence of Y_E on y_{22} for the transistor and circuit in Example 5-7.

Solution

From (86),

$$y_{22} = g_{22} + jb_{22} = y_o - \frac{(y_o + y_f)y_o}{(y_i + y_f + y_o) + Y_E} \tag{96}$$

Let

$$P'' + jQ'' = M'' \ \underline{/\theta''} = (y_o + y_f)y_o$$
$$= (14.66 + j7.83)10^{-6} = 16.6 \times 10^{-6} \ \underline{/28.1°} \tag{97}$$

and, as before,

$$y_o' = g_o' + jb_o' = (y_i + y_f + y_o)$$
$$= (12.51 - j15.9)10^{-3} \tag{98}$$

It is seen that $g_o > 0$ and $g_o' > 0$, and

$$C = \frac{M''}{2g_o g_o' - P''} = -1.15 \tag{99}$$

Since $C < 0$, it is possible for g_{22} to become negative for some value of Y_E. The U and jV axes intercepts for the $g_{22} = 0$ line are

$$U_{\text{intercept}} = -\frac{2g_o g_o' - P''}{P''} = +0.984 \tag{100}$$

$$V_{\text{intercept}} = \frac{2g_o g_o' - P''}{Q''} = -1.84 \tag{101}$$

Also,

$$\phi = \tan^{-1} \frac{Q''}{-P''} = \tan^{-1} \frac{7.83}{-14.66} = 180° - 28.1° \tag{102}$$

$$X = \frac{1}{C} = -0.87 \tag{103}$$

The $g_{22} = 0$ line is drawn in Fig. 5-10. To make $g_{22} > 0$ for $g_E = 0.5$, $b_E < -2.65$ and $b_E > +70$ (approximately, because the chart is not highly detailed in this latter region). The smaller value leads to negative capacitance (which suggests using inductance in the emitter circuit for stability) and the larger value to $C_E = 0.89/\omega$. Thus, $g_{22} > 0$ if $C_E > 0.89/\omega$, and this much capacitance also makes $g_{11} > 0$ for $g_E = 0.5$. Also

$$G_E = \frac{1}{R_E} = g_E g_o' = 0.5(12.51)10^{-3} = 6.25 \times 10^{-3}$$

or

$$R_E \cong 160 \ \Omega$$

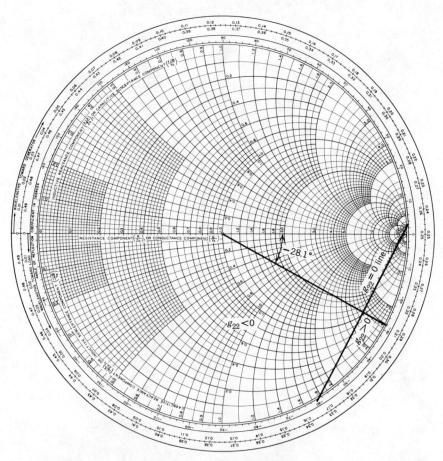

Figure 5-10.   Location of the $g_{22} = 0$ line for Example 5-8.

and

$$\omega C_E > 0.89 \text{ for stability,}$$

or

$$\frac{1}{\omega C_E} < \frac{1}{0.89} = 1.12 \ \Omega$$

If ωC_E is selected equal to 1, it turns out that the circuit is stable. However, observe that the reactance of C_E is only 0.00625 times R_E. Suppose that, according to the design rule-of-thumb, $1/\omega C_E$ is selected to be one-tenth of $R_E = 160 \ \Omega$, that is, 16 Ω. Then

$$B_E = \omega C_E = \frac{1}{16} = 0.0625$$

and

$$b_E = \frac{B_E + b'_o}{g'_o} = \frac{(62.5 - 15.9)}{12.51} = 3.72$$

This makes $g_{22} < 0$ and the circuit becomes potentially unstable. This means that some value of Y_L can cause Re $Y_{in} = g_{in}$ to be negative. This is investigated in Example 5-9.

Example 5-9

Examine how Y_L influences G_{in} when $R_E = 160 \ \Omega$ and $1/\omega C_E = 16 \ \Omega$.

Solution

$$Y_{in} = y_{11} - \frac{y_{12} y_{21}}{y_{22} + Y_L} \qquad (104)$$

so it is necessary to calculate the overall parameters. Using (83), (84), (85), and (86), with

$$Y_E = (6.25 + j62.5)10^{-3}$$

and, for convenience in calculations,

$$\frac{1}{(y_i + y_r + y_f + y_o) + Y_E} = 7.41 - j18.42$$

it is found that

$$y_{11} = (2.22 + j3.68)10^{-3} \qquad y_{12} = -(23.9 + j48.4)10^{-6}$$

$$y_{21} = (19.0 - j19.3)10^{-3} \qquad y_{22} = (-0.244 + j1.01)10^{-3}$$

The Smith chart coordinates become

$$g + jb = \frac{G_L}{g_{22}} + j\frac{B_L + b_{22}}{g_{22}} \tag{105}$$

But $g_{22} < 0$ in this example; therefore the *g values are negative* (for positive G_L) and the *b values and angles are opposite in sign* to those on the Smith chart.
  Let

$$P_1 + jQ_1 = y_{12}y_{21} \tag{106}$$

Then (104), (105), and (106) combine to give

$$G_{in} = g_{11} - \frac{P_1(g+1) + Q_1 b}{g_{22}\left[(g+1)^2 + b^2\right]} \tag{107}$$

The equation for the $G_{in} = 0$ contour in terms of g and b can be obtained from (107) by setting $G_{in} = 0$. This results in

$$\left[g - \left(\frac{P_1}{2g_{11}g_{22}} - 1\right)\right]^2 + \left[b - \frac{Q_1}{2g_{11}g_{22}}\right]^2 = \left(\frac{P_1}{2g_{11}g_{22}}\right)^2 + \left(\frac{Q_1}{2g_{11}g_{22}}\right)^2$$

$$\tag{108}$$

which is a circle in the $g - jb$ plane representing the values of g and b, which make $G_{in} = 0$. When $g_{22} > 0$ and $g > 0$, (108) transforms into the straight line in the $U - jV$ plane for $G_{in} = 0$. Unfortunately, when $g_{22} < 0$ and $g < 0$, (108) transforms into a curved contour in the $U - jV$ plane for $G_{in} = 0$. In this example, if the values of g and b that satisfy (108) are plotted on the Smith chart, the actual $G_{in} = 0$ contour is obtained. This is done by solving (108) for b to obtain

$$b = \frac{Q_1}{2g_{11}g_{22}} \pm \sqrt{\frac{P_1^2 + Q_1^2}{(2g_{11}g_{22})^2} - \left[g + \left(1 - \frac{P_1}{2g_{11}g_{22}}\right)\right]^2} \tag{109}$$

Then assume different negative values for g and for each calculate two values of b using the $+$ and $-$ signs in (109). The results are given in Table 5-4 and plotted in Fig. 5-11.

g	b_1	b_2
0	−0.89	1.8
−0.2	−0.83	1.7
−0.5	−0.67	1.5
−0.75	−0.44	1.3
−1.0	0	0.85
−1.05	0.20	0.65
−1.07	0.43	0.43

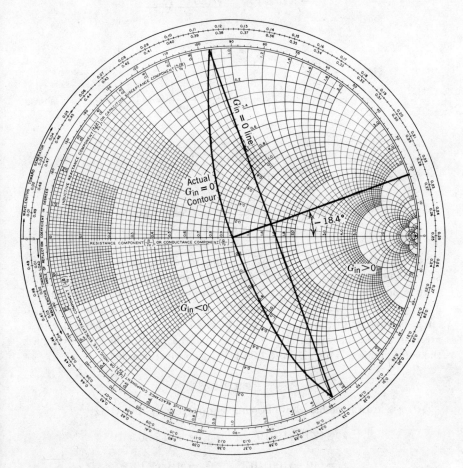

Figure 5-11.   The $G_{in} = 0$ contour for Example 5-9. $g < 0$, and signs of b and angles reversed because $g_{22} < 0$.

135

Other values of g and b substituted into (107) quickly indicate where $G_{in} < 0$ and $G_{in} > 0$.

Since the sign associated with g is not important when $g = 0$, the actual $G_{in} = 0$ contour intersects the $G_{in} = 0$ line (calculated as before but with $g_{22} < 0$) at two points on the $g = 0$ circle.

Various calculated values are

$$P_1 + jQ_1 = M_1 \quad \underline{/\theta} = y_{12}y_{21}$$

$$= (-1.388 - j0.461)10^{-6}$$

$$= 1.46 \times 10^{-6} \quad \underline{/180° + 18.4°}$$

$$C = \frac{M_1}{2g_{11}g_{22} - P_1} = 4.75 \qquad X = \frac{1}{C} = 0.21$$

$$\phi = \tan^{-1}\frac{Q_1}{-P_1} = \tan^{-1}\frac{-0.461}{1.388} = -18.4°$$

$$U_{\text{intercept}} = -\frac{2g_{11}g_{22} - P_1}{P_1} = 0.222$$

$$V_{\text{intercept}} = \frac{2g_{11}g_{22} - P_1}{Q_1} = 0.668$$

Since $g_{22} < 0$, the regions of stability and instability on either side of the $G_{in} = 0$ line are opposite to what is expected from previous examples.

It is noticed from the actual $G_{in} = 0$ contour that the circuit is stable if $g < -1.07$ or $G_L > 1.07 |g_{22}| = 0.26 \times 10^{-3}$ mho. This is because the $g = -1.07$ circle is tangent to the $G_{in} = 0$ contour (or from Table 5-4 where b_1 and b_2 are equal) and the values of g more negative than -1.07 lie entirely within the stable region. Thus, if $R_L < 3.83$ kΩ the circuit is stable.

PROBLEMS

5-1. A transistor has the following parameters at 400 MHz:

$$y_{ie} = (20 + j10)10^{-3} \qquad y_{re} = (-1 - j0.5)10^{-3}$$

$$y_{fe} = (40 - j100)10^{-3} \qquad y_{oe} = (1 + j5)10^{-3}$$

(a) Is the transistor active?

(b) Is the transistor inherently stable?

(c) Find $(G_p)_{max}$ in decibels.

(d) Calculate G_{oo} in decibels.

(e) Draw power-gain circles for G_p of 1, 3, and 5 dB below $(G_p)_{max}$.

(f) Find the optimum source and load terminations.

5-2. Repeat 5-1 for the following parameters at 60 MHz:

$$y_{ie} = (6.8 + j6.1)10^{-3} \qquad y_{re} = (-j0.81)10^{-3}$$

$$y_{fe} = (33.6 - j44.2)10^{-3} \qquad y_{oe} = (1.24 + j1.92)10^{-3}$$

5-3. For the transistor of Problem 5-2 determine Y_L, to obtain the greatest power gain with $\delta = 0.3$ and estimate the value for this power gain in decibels from power-gain circles.

5-4. Construct an input admittance grid for the transistor of Problem 5-2 and determine $(Y_s)_{opt}$ and compare with the result of Problem 5-2.

5-5. (a) Construct a normalized input admittance grid for the transistor of Problem 5-2 and determine Y_s when Y_L makes $\delta = 0.3$. (b) Calculate bandwidths expected for $\delta = 0.3$.

5-6. The parameters of a transistor are

$$y_{ie} = (20 + j10)10^{-3} \qquad y_{re} = (-1 - j0.5)10^{-3}$$

$$y_{fe} = (40 - j100)10^{-3} \qquad y_{oe} = (1 + j5)10^{-3}$$

Draw a $G_{in} = 0$ line for the transistor when used as an emitter follower and identify stable and unstable regions. How much emitter resistance ensures stability?

5-7. The parameters of a transistor are

$$y_{ie} = (2 + j2)10^{-3} \qquad y_{re} = (-2 - j20)10^{-6}$$

$$y_{fe} = (20 - j3)10^{-3} \qquad y_{oe} = (20 + j60)10^{-6}$$

Draw a $G_{in} = 0$ line for the transistor when used as a CE amplifier and identify stable and unstable regions. How much load resistance ensures stability?

5-8. Draw several power-gain circles for the transistor amplifier of Problem 5-7.

5-9.   A transistor whose parameters at 30 MHz are

$$y_{ie} = (2+j2)10^{-3} \qquad y_{re} = (-0.01-j0.3)10^{-3}$$

$$y_{fe} = (140-j58)10^{-3} \qquad y_{oe} = (0.01+j0.2)10^{-3}$$

is used in the amplifier shown in Fig. 5.12.
What range of values for R_E assures that $g_{11} > 0$?

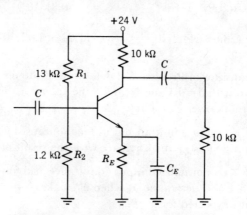

Figure 5-12.   Circuit for Problem 5-9.

5-10.   In problem 5-9, let $R_E = 150$ Ω and choose the reactance of C_E equal
to 0.1 R_E at 30 MHz.
(*a*)   Calculate C_E.
(*b*)   Calculate the overall parameters at 30 MHz.
(*c*)   Draw the $G_{in} = 0$ line or contour and identify regions of stability
and instability. Determine the circuit stability with and without the
effect of R_1 and R_2.
(*d*)   Is it possible to make $G_{in} > 0$ at 30 MHz by placing a capacitor
across the output load resistor? If so, what minimum value is needed?

5-11.   In Problem 5-9, can some passive Y_E combination make the overall
parameter $y_{12} = 0$? If so, is the resulting circuit inherently stable?

5-12.   In Problem 5-9, what passive Y_E combination maximizes the overall
parameter y_{21}?

CHAPTER SIX

SCATTERING PARAMETERS

6-0 INTRODUCTION

Scattering implies causing something to separate into different components, and scattering parameters provide a measure of the degree of separation and the magnitudes of the different components.

Scattering is relatively easy to visualize when the scattered components actually exist. For example, when light falls on an atom, the electronic motions are changed such that light is reemitted. This reemitted light is called scattered light, and its amplitude is related to a scattering constant of the atom. It turns out that the intensity of scattered light is inversely proportional to the fourth power of the wavelength. This explains why the sky is blue rather than red because the factor $1/\lambda^4$ is about 10 times larger for blue than for red. The blue coloring in certain animals and birds arises more often from scattering of reflected light than from blue pigment. Similarly, most of the greens found in the skins of fish and reptiles are accounted for by scattered blue light emerging through a layer of yellow pigment.

There is an acoustical analog of the above optical scattering law. When the size of an obstacle is small compared with the wavelength of impinging sound, the higher intensities of the scattered sound are produced by the higher frequencies. This explains why a grove of trees appears to raise the pitch of scattered sound.

In 1911, Rutherford worked out the theory of scattering of alpha particles by matter. To him goes credit for proving the existence of compact nuclei in atoms. In 1923, Compton scattered x-rays from electrons in an atomic

139

structure. Some of the energy of the impinging photons would be delivered to an electron. The scattered photon, having less energy than initially, had a new lower frequency that depended on a scattering angle. In 1928, Raman obtained information about molecular vibrational and rotational energy states of transparent substances by observing the scattering of incident monochromatic light. The scattered radiation consisted of additional frequencies above and below the original and separated by an amount characteristic of the various energy states.

The successes of radar and other communication systems depend on the reflected and scattered waves established by the targets and objects in space. Reflected waves can occur on transmission lines and in waveguides. In all such cases, a clear distinction can be made between the incident and reflected or scattered components because they exist and move in different directions following well-known laws of behavior.

The scattering concept is more difficult to visualize when the incident and reflected components do not actually exist. This is true for a transistor connected to its load through a lumped matching network. Here, it is necessary to define what is meant by "incident" and "reflected" components because they cannot be identified otherwise. Therefore, the incident current is defined as the current that the transistor would deliver to a conjugate matched load. The fact that the matching network, which is actually connected to the transistor, may not necessarily provide a conjugate-matched load, does not alter the validity of the incident-current definition. Since the incident current can be different from the actual current delivered to the matching network, their difference is defined as the reflected current. Defining statements are also made for incident and reflected voltages.

Therefore, when the scattering concept is applied to lumped circuits, the actual currents and voltages can be separated into scattered components according to appropriate definitions. It is desirable, however, that such definitions should lead ultimately to relationships that prove useful in the analysis and design of circuits and in the laboratory measurements of the parameters that describe the scattering. The above definitions for incident and reflected currents are particularly suitable for such purposes.

6-1 THE ONE-PORT NETWORK

The scattering concept is perhaps best illustrated by considering the one-port network shown in Fig. 6-1. The actual current and voltage are

$$I = \frac{E}{Z_o + Z_L} \tag{1}$$

and

$$V = \frac{EZ_L}{Z_o + Z_L} \tag{2}$$

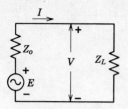

Figure 6-1. One-port network.

in which Z_o is considered to be the internal impedance of the generator.

The "incident" components are obtained when the generator is connected to a conjugate matched load Z_o^* as in Fig. 6-2. Thus

$$I_i = \frac{E}{Z_o + Z_o^*} = \frac{E}{2\,\mathrm{Re}\,Z_o} \tag{3}$$

and

$$V_i = \frac{EZ_o^*}{Z_o + Z_o^*} = \frac{EZ_o^*}{2\,\mathrm{Re}\,Z_o} \tag{4}$$

where Re stands for "real part of."

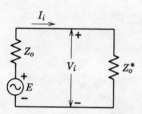

Figure 6-2. Generator with conjugate matched load used to define the "incident" components I_i and V_i.

The "reflected" components are calculated using the defining decomposition equations

$$I = I_i - I_r \tag{5}$$

and

$$V = V_i + V_r \tag{6}$$

Using (1) and (3) in (5), we find that the "reflected" current is

$$I_r = I_i - I$$

$$= \left(\frac{Z_L - Z_o^*}{Z_L + Z_o} \right) I_i$$

$$= S^I I_i \tag{7}$$

where $S^I = (Z_L - Z_o^*)/(Z_L + Z_o)$ is a current scattering parameter for the one-port circuit. Similarly, using (2) and (4) in (6), the "reflected" voltage is

$$V_r = V - V_i$$

$$= \frac{Z_o}{Z_o^*}\left(\frac{Z_L - Z_o^*}{Z_L + Z_o}\right)V_i$$

$$= \frac{Z_o}{Z_o^*}S^I V_i = S^V V_i \tag{8}$$

where $S^V = (Z_o/Z_o^*)S^I$ is a voltage scattering parameter for the one-port circuit. It is also readily shown that

$$V_i = Z_o^* I_i \tag{9a}$$

and

$$V_r = Z_o I_r \tag{9b}$$

The incident and reflected components are related to each other through the impedances and the scattering parameters as defined. Each scattering parameter and reflected component are zero when $Z_L = Z_o^*$.

It is important to make some additional comments about the impedance Z_o. This impedance is often made to be a pure resistance $R_o > 0$, so that $Z_o = R_o$, and it is used as a normalizing or reference resistance. In high-frequency situations where 50-Ω transmission-line interconnections are practical, it is usual to consider the reference resistance equal to 50 Ω, particularly if scattering-parameter measurements are made using 50-Ω lines and terminations.

If $Z_o = R_o$, and $Z_o^* = R_o$, then

$$S^I = S^V = \frac{Z_L - R_o}{Z_L + R_o} \tag{10}$$

For this case, the current and voltage scattering parameters of the one-port circuit are equal and have the same form exactly as the reflection coefficient of a transmission line having a characteristic resistance R_o and terminated in a load Z_L. The scattering parameters of the port are equal to zero if its impedance is the same as the reference resistance R_o. Also, for this case, (9a) and (9b) become

$$V_i = R_o I_i \tag{11a}$$

and

$$V_r = R_o I_r \tag{11b}$$

Example 6-1

A load impedance $200 - j100$ Ω is connected to a signal source whose internal impedance is $50 + j0$ Ω. Determine the current and voltage scattering parameters S^I and S^V.

Solution

Since $R_o = 50$ Ω (a pure resistance), the current and voltage scattering parameters are equal. Thus,

$$S^I = S^V = \frac{Z_L - R_o}{Z_L + R_o} = \frac{(Z_L / R_o) - 1}{(Z_L / R_o) + 1}$$

$$= \frac{3 - j2}{5 - j2} = 0.67 \; \underline{/-11.9°}$$

Notice that if the normalized load impedance $Z_L / R_o = 4 - j2$ is located on the Smith chart, the resulting reflection coefficient read from the chart is the same as S^I and S^V above.

6-2 THE n-PORT NETWORK

The scattering parameters for the n-port network shown in Fig. 6.3 will be developed using matrix algebra. It is assumed that the individual generators are independent of each other. This means that the matrix $[Z_o]$ representing internal impedances contains no cross-coupling terms, and is given by the diagonal matrix

$$[Z_o] = \begin{bmatrix} Z_{o1} & 0 & \cdots & 0 \\ 0 & Z_{o2} & \cdots & 0 \\ \vdots & \vdots & & \vdots \\ 0 & 0 & \cdots & Z_{on} \end{bmatrix} \tag{12}$$

The incident and reflected components at the ports are related to the actual voltages and currents by the column matrices

$$[I] = [I_i] - [I_r] \tag{13a}$$

and

$$[V] = [V_i] + [V_r] \tag{13b}$$

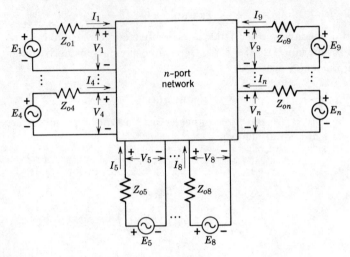

Figure 6-3. An n-port network with generators.

The incident and reflected components are related by

$$[V_i] = [Z_o^*][I_i] \qquad (14a)$$

and

$$[V_r] = [Z_o][I_r] \qquad (14b)$$

which correspond to the one-port case.

The open-circuit impedance-parameter relationship for the n-port network is

$$[V] = [z][I] \qquad (15)$$

The incident and reflected components can be determined from (12), (13), (14), and (15) as follows:

$$[V_r] = [V] - [V_i] = [z][I] - [Z_o^*][I_i]$$

or

$$[Z_o][I_r] = [z]([I_i] - [I_r]) - [Z_o^*][I_i]$$

Combine terms to obtain

$$([z] + [Z_o])[I_r] = ([z] - [Z_o^*])[I_i]$$

Multiply from the left by $([z]+[Z_o])^{-1}$ to obtain

$$[I_r] = ([z]+[Z_o])^{-1}([z]-[Z_o^*])[I_i]$$

$$= [S^I][I_i] \tag{16}$$

where

$$[S^I] = ([z]+[Z_o])^{-1}([z]-[Z_o^*]) \tag{16a}$$

is the current scattering-parameter matrix that is analogous to that for the one-port given in (7).

Similarly, using the short-circuit admittance-parameter relationship

$$[I] = [y][V] \tag{17}$$

it is found that

$$[V_r] = -([Y_o]+[y])^{-1}([y]-[Y_o^*])[V_i]$$

$$= [S^V][V_i] \tag{18}$$

where

$$[y] = [z]^{-1}, \ [Y_o] = [Z_o]^{-1},$$

and

$$[S^V] = -([Y_o]+[y])^{-1}([y]-[Y_o^*]) \tag{19}$$

is the voltage scattering-parameter matrix.

Example 6-2

A transistor whose impedance parameters are

$$[z] = \begin{bmatrix} z_i & z_r \\ z_f & z_o \end{bmatrix}$$

is connected between source and load resistances both equal to R_o. Determine the current scattering matrix $[S^I]$.

Solution

From (16a),

$$[S^I] = ([z]+[Z_o])^{-1}([z]-[Z_o^*])$$

The matrix of internal impedances is

$$[Z_o] = \begin{bmatrix} R_o & 0 \\ 0 & R_o \end{bmatrix} = [Z_o^*]$$

then

$$[z] + [Z_o] = \begin{bmatrix} z_i + R_o & z_r \\ z_f & z_o + R_o \end{bmatrix}$$

The matrix $([z] + [Z_o])^{-1}$ is the inverse of $([z] + [Z_o])$. The inverse matrix is found by dividing the determinant of the original matrix into the transpose of the matrix formed by replacing each element of the original matrix by its cofactor.

The determinant of the original matrix is

$$(z_i + R_o)(z_o + R_o) - z_r z_f$$

The cofactor matrix is

$$\begin{bmatrix} z_o + R_o & -z_f \\ -z_r & z_i + R_o \end{bmatrix}$$

The transpose of the cofactor matrix is

$$\begin{bmatrix} z_o + R_o & -z_r \\ -z_f & z_i + R_o \end{bmatrix}$$

Therefore, the inverse matrix is

$$([z] + [Z_o])^{-1} = \frac{1}{(z_i + R_o)(z_o + R_o) - z_r z_f} \begin{bmatrix} z_o + R_o & -z_r \\ -z_f & z_i + R_o \end{bmatrix}$$

The other matrix involved is

$$([z] - [Z_o^*]) = \begin{bmatrix} z_i - R_o & z_r \\ z_f & z_o - R_o \end{bmatrix}$$

Then, finally,

$$[S^I] = \frac{1}{(z_i + R_o)(z_o + R_o) - z_r z_f} \begin{bmatrix} z_o + R_o & -z_r \\ -z_f & z_i + R_o \end{bmatrix} \begin{bmatrix} z_i - R_o & z_r \\ z_f & z_o - R_o \end{bmatrix}$$

$$= \frac{1}{(z_i + R_o)(z_o + R_o) - z_r z_f} \begin{bmatrix} (z_o + R_o)(z_i - R_o) - z_r z_f & 2z_r R_o \\ 2z_f R_o & (z_i + R_o)(z_o - R_o) - z_r z_f \end{bmatrix}$$

represents the current scattering parameter matrix.

6-3 NORMALIZED SCATTERING PARAMETERS

It is convenient to define normalized incident and reflected components by

$$[a] = \frac{1}{\sqrt{2}} ([Z_o] + [Z_o^*])^{1/2} [I_i]$$

$$= [\operatorname{Re} Z_o]^{1/2} [I_i] \tag{20}$$

and

$$[b] = \frac{1}{\sqrt{2}} ([Z_o] + [Z_o^*])^{1/2} [I_r]$$

$$= [\operatorname{Re} Z_o]^{1/2} [I_r] \tag{21}$$

where

$$\frac{1}{\sqrt{2}} ([Z_o] + [Z_o^*])^{1/2} = [\operatorname{Re} Z_o]^{1/2}$$

$$= \begin{bmatrix} \sqrt{\operatorname{Re} Z_{o1}} & 0 & \cdots & 0 \\ 0 & \sqrt{\operatorname{Re} Z_{o2}} & \cdots & 0 \\ \vdots & \vdots & & \vdots \\ 0 & 0 & \cdots & \sqrt{\operatorname{Re} Z_{on}} \end{bmatrix} \tag{22}$$

Then, combining (16) with (20) and (21),

$$[\operatorname{Re} Z_o]^{-1/2} [b] = [I_r] = [S^I][I_i]$$

$$= [S^I][\operatorname{Re} Z_o]^{-1/2} [a]$$

Solving for $[b]$ yields

$$[b] = [\operatorname{Re}Z_o]^{1/2}[S^I][\operatorname{Re}Z_o]^{-1/2}[a]$$

or

$$[b] = [S][a] \tag{23}$$

where

$$[\operatorname{Re}Z_o]^{-1/2} = \begin{bmatrix} \dfrac{1}{\sqrt{\operatorname{Re}Z_{o1}}} & 0 & \cdots & 0 \\[2ex] 0 & \dfrac{1}{\sqrt{\operatorname{Re}Z_{o2}}} & \cdots & 0 \\[2ex] \vdots & \vdots & & \vdots \\[2ex] 0 & 0 & \cdots & \dfrac{1}{\sqrt{\operatorname{Re}Z_{on}}} \end{bmatrix} \tag{24}$$

and

$$[S] = [\operatorname{Re}Z_o]^{1/2}[S^I][\operatorname{Re}Z_o]^{-1/2} \tag{25}$$

The matrix $[S]$ thus obtained is called the normalized scattering matrix, and its elements are called normalized scattering parameters, or simply scattering parameters. These are the parameters that are usually meant when reference is made to scattering parameters.

The scattering parameters can be calculated using (16a) and (25) for the original n-port network (whose z parameters exist) which has been effectively enlarged or augmented by the normalizing impedances (Problem 6-1). The normalizing impedances are considered to be the internal impedances of the generators. Thus the scattering parameters involve not only the original n-port network but also the augmenting impedances, and they apply to this entire arrangement called the augmented n-port network.

It can be shown that

$$[S^I] = [Z_o]^{-1}[S^V][Z_o^*] \tag{26}$$

If the impedance matrix does not exist for a particular n-port network, but the admittance matrix exists, then the scattering parameters can be calculated using (19), (25), and (26) (Problem 6-2).

Different normalizing impedances used with the same n-port network lead to different sets of scattering parameters as determined by (25). It is clear that some general agreement should be desirable about what normalizing impedances to use in order to eliminate this source of confusion. Knowledge of the scattering parameters only for some n-port netwrok is not particularly valuable without also knowing the associated normalizing impedances.

It will be advantageous to agree to make the normalizing impedances equal to pure resistances. Furthermore, the numerical values of these normalizing or reference resistances will be determined primarily by the values that are most suitable for practical laboratory measurements of scattering parameters.

Therefore, if $[Z_o] = [Z_o^*] = [R_o]$, then

$$[S^I] = ([z] + [R_o])^{-1}([z] - [R_o]) \tag{27}$$

and

$$[S] = [R_o]^{1/2}[S^I][R_o]^{-1/2} \tag{28}$$

Expansion of (28) shows that

$$[S] = [S^I] \tag{29}$$

if the reference resistances at all ports are equal.

The normalized incident and reflected component relationships for an augmented three-port network are found from (23) to be

$$\begin{bmatrix} b_1 \\ b_2 \\ b_3 \end{bmatrix} = \begin{bmatrix} S_{11} & S_{12} & S_{13} \\ S_{21} & S_{22} & S_{23} \\ S_{31} & S_{32} & S_{33} \end{bmatrix} \begin{bmatrix} a_1 \\ a_2 \\ a_3 \end{bmatrix} \tag{30}$$

6-31 Parameter Conversions

Using the typical conditions

$$[Z_o] = [Z_o^*] = \left[\frac{1}{Y_o}\right] = [R_o] \tag{31}$$

with all normalizing resistances equal, results in

$$[S] = [S^I] = [S^V] \tag{32}$$

Thus, (16a) becomes

$$([z] + [R_o])[S] = [z] - [R_o] \tag{33}$$

Solve for $[z]$ to obtain

$$[z] = [R_o]([I] + [S])([I] - [S])^{-1} \tag{34}$$

where $[I]$ is the unit diagonal matrix. Since $[R_o]$ has equal values along the diagonal, (34) becomes

$$[z'] = \left[\frac{z}{R_o} \right] = ([I] + [S])([I] - [S])^{-1} \tag{35}$$

where $[z']$ represents the normalized parameters found by dividing the actual z parameters by R_o. Expansion of (35) yields the conversion relationships from S to z' parameters given in Table 6-1.

Also, using (31) and (32), (19) becomes

$$([Y_o] + [y])[S] = -([y] - [Y_o]) \tag{36}$$

Solve for $[y]$ to obtain

$$[y] = [Y_o]([I] - [S])([I] + [S])^{-1} \tag{37}$$

where $[I]$ is the unit diagonal matrix. Since $[Y_o]$ has equal values along the diagonal, (37) becomes

$$[y'] = [R_o y] = ([I] - [S])([I] + [S])^{-1} \tag{38}$$

where $[y']$ represents the normalized parameters found by multiplying the actual y parameters by R_o. Expansion of (38) yields the conversion relationships from S to y' parameters given in Table 6-1.

Other conversions from S to h' parameters are also given in Table 6-1.

6-4 CALCULATION OF SCATTERING PARAMETERS

Consider the two-port network augmented by reference resistances R_{o1} and R_{o2} shown in Fig. 6-4. Total, incident, reflected, and normalized components are marked for convenience. The scattering parameters can be determined more directly from (23) than from (28). Thus, since

$$b_1 = S_{11}a_1 + S_{12}a_2 \tag{39}$$

$$b_2 = S_{21}a_1 + S_{22}a_2 \tag{40}$$

TABLE 6-1 CONVERSIONS INVOLVING SCATTERING PARAMETERS

S Parameters in terms of Normalized $z, y,$ and h Parameters	Normalized $z, y,$ and h Parameters in terms of S Parameters

$$S_{11} = \frac{(z_i' - 1)(z_o' + 1) - z_r' z_f'}{(1 + z_i')(1 + z_o') - z_r' z_f'}$$

$$z_i' = \frac{(1 + S_{11})(1 - S_{22}) + S_{12}S_{21}}{(1 - S_{11})(1 - S_{22}) - S_{12}S_{21}}$$

$$S_{12} = \frac{2z_r'}{(1 + z_i')(1 + z_o') - z_r' z_f'}$$

$$z_r' = \frac{2S_{12}}{(1 - S_{11})(1 - S_{22}) - S_{12}S_{21}}$$

$$S_{21} = \frac{2z_f'}{(1 + z_i')(1 + z_o') - z_r' z_f'}$$

$$z_f' = \frac{2S_{21}}{(1 - S_{11})(1 - S_{22}) - S_{12}S_{21}}$$

$$S_{22} = \frac{(z_i' + 1)(z_o' - 1) - z_r' z_f'}{(1 + z_i')(1 + z_o') - z_r' z_f'}$$

$$z_o' = \frac{(1 - S_{11})(1 + S_{22}) + S_{12}S_{21}}{(1 - S_{11})(1 - S_{22}) - S_{12}S_{21}}$$

$$S_{11} = \frac{(1 - y_i')(1 + y_o') + y_r' y_f'}{(1 + y_i')(1 + y_o') - y_r' y_f'}$$

$$y_i' = \frac{(1 - S_{11})(1 + S_{22}) + S_{12}S_{21}}{(1 + S_{11})(1 + S_{22}) - S_{12}S_{21}}$$

$$S_{12} = \frac{-2y_r'}{(1 + y_i')(1 + y_o') - y_r' y_f'}$$

$$y_r' = \frac{-2S_{12}}{(1 + S_{11})(1 + S_{22}) - S_{12}S_{21}}$$

$$S_{21} = \frac{-2y_f'}{(1 + y_i')(1 + y_o') - y_r' y_f'}$$

$$y_f' = \frac{-2S_{21}}{(1 + S_{11})(1 + S_{22}) - S_{12}S_{21}}$$

$$S_{22} = \frac{(1 + y_i')(1 - y_o') + y_r' y_f'}{(1 + y_i')(1 + y_o') - y_r' y_f'}$$

$$y_o' = \frac{(1 + S_{11})(1 - S_{22}) + S_{12}S_{21}}{(1 + S_{11})(1 + S_{22}) - S_{12}S_{21}}$$

$$S_{11} = \frac{(h_i' - 1)(1 + h_o') - h_r' h_f'}{(1 + h_i')(1 + h_o') - h_r' h_f'}$$

$$h_i' = \frac{(1 + S_{11})(1 + S_{22}) - S_{12}S_{21}}{(1 - S_{11})(1 + S_{22}) + S_{12}S_{21}}$$

$$S_{12} = \frac{2h_r'}{(1 + h_i')(1 + h_o') - h_r' h_f'}$$

$$h_r' = \frac{2S_{12}}{(1 - S_{11})(1 + S_{22}) + S_{12}S_{21}}$$

$$S_{21} = \frac{-2h_f'}{(1 + h_i')(1 + h_o') - h_r' h_f'}$$

$$h_f' = \frac{-2S_{21}}{(1 - S_{11})(1 + S_{22}) + S_{12}S_{21}}$$

$$S_{22} = \frac{(1 + h_i')(1 - h_o') + h_r' h_f'}{(1 + h_i')(1 + h_o') - h_r' h_f'}$$

$$h_o' = \frac{(1 - S_{11})(1 - S_{22}) - S_{12}S_{21}}{(1 - S_{11})(1 + S_{22}) + S_{12}S_{21}}$$

The primed $z, y,$ and h parameters used above are found from the actual $z, y,$ and h parameters normalized to R_o as follows:

$$z_i' = \frac{z_i}{R_o} \qquad y_i' = R_o y_i \qquad h_i' = \frac{h_i}{R_o}$$

$$z_r' = \frac{z_r}{R_o} \qquad y_r' = R_o y_r \qquad h_r' = h_r$$

$$z_f' = \frac{z_f}{R_o} \qquad y_f' = R_o y_f \qquad h_f' = h_f$$

$$z_o' = \frac{z_o}{R_o} \qquad y_o' = R_o y_o \qquad h_o' = R_o h_o$$

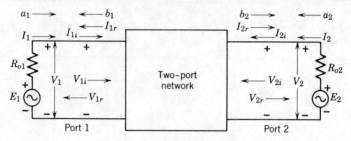

Figure 6-4.   A two-port network augmented by reference resistances.

the scattering parameters are given by

$$S_{11} = \frac{b_1}{a_1}\bigg|_{a_2=0} \quad (41); \qquad S_{12} = \frac{b_1}{a_2}\bigg|_{a_1=0} \qquad (42)$$

$$S_{21} = \frac{b_2}{a_1}\bigg|_{a_2=0} \quad (43); \qquad S_{22} = \frac{b_2}{a_2}\bigg|_{a_1=0} \qquad (44)$$

In order to satisfy the requirement $a_2=0$, reference to (20) indicates that $I_{2i}=0$. Two conditions must be met to make $I_{2i}=0$. The first is $E_2=0$, which means that no external voltage source is connected to port 2 to cause an incident current. The second condition is that port 2 is terminated in the reference resistance R_{o2} so that $V_2 = -R_{o2}I_2$. Now, using (13 and 14),

$$V_2 + R_{o2}I_2 = V_{2i} + V_{2r} + R_{o2}(I_{2i} - I_{2r})$$

$$= R_{o2}I_{2i} + R_{o2}I_{2r} + R_{o2}I_{2i} - R_{o2}I_{2r}$$

$$= 2R_{o2}I_{2i}$$

$$= 2\sqrt{R_{o2}}\, a_2 \qquad (45)$$

or

$$a_2 = \frac{V_2 + R_{o2}I_2}{2\sqrt{R_{o2}}} \qquad (46)$$

Since $V_2 = -R_{o2}I_2$, then $a_2=0$ and $I_{2i}=0$ as required. This means that the generator at port 1 cannot cause a reflected current from R_{o2} which in turn would act as an incident current at port 2. Since $I_{2i}=0$, it is noticed that $I_2 = -I_{2r}$.

Similarly, the requirement $a_1 = 0$ is satisfied when $E_1 = 0$ and port 1 is terminated in reference resistance R_{o1}. In this case, it is found that

$$a_1 = \frac{V_1 + R_{o1}I_1}{2\sqrt{R_{o1}}} \tag{47}$$

For an n-port network, (46) and (47) become

$$[a] = \tfrac{1}{2}[R_o]^{-1/2}([V] + [R_o][I]) \tag{48}$$

If an n-port network has arbitrary terminating impedances $[Z']$, then

$$[a'] = \tfrac{1}{2}[\mathrm{Re}\,Z']^{-1/2}([V] + [Z'][I]) \tag{49}$$

where the prime (') is used to distinguish the values from the case where the reference-resistance terminations are used.

Useful relationships involving the normalized reflected components are developed as follows. Using (13 and 14) again,

$$V_1 - R_{o1}I_1 = V_{1i} + V_{1r} - R_{o1}(I_{1i} - I_{1r})$$

$$= R_{o1}I_{1i} + R_{o1}I_{1r} - R_{o1}I_{1i} + R_{o1}I_{1r}$$

$$= 2R_{o1}I_{1r}$$

$$= 2\sqrt{R_{o1}}\, b_1 \tag{50}$$

or

$$b_1 = \frac{V_1 - R_{o1}I_1}{2\sqrt{R_{o1}}} \tag{51}$$

Similarly,

$$b_2 = \frac{V_2 - R_{o2}I_2}{2\sqrt{R_{o2}}} \tag{52}$$

For an n-port network, (51) and (52) become

$$[b] = \tfrac{1}{2}[R_o]^{-1/2}([V] - [R_o][I]) \tag{53}$$

Equations (48) and (53) provide the relationships between normalized incident and reflected components and the terminal voltages and currents.

If an n-port network has arbitrary terminating impedances $[Z']$, then

$$[b'] = \tfrac{1}{2}[\operatorname{Re} Z']^{-1/2}([V] - [Z'^*][I])$$ (54)

where the prime ($'$) again distinguishes the values from the case where the reference resistance terminations are used.

Having identified how to satisfy the circuit requirements for making $a_1 = 0$ or $a_2 = 0$, the scattering parameters can be evaluated using (41), (42), (43), and (44) as follows:

$$S_{11} = \left.\frac{b_1}{a_1}\right|_{a_2=0} = \left.\frac{\sqrt{R_{o1}}\, I_{1r}}{\sqrt{R_{o1}}\, I_{1i}}\right|_{I_{2i}=0} = \left.\frac{I_{1r}}{I_{1i}}\right|_{I_{2i}=0} = \left.\frac{V_{1r}}{V_{1i}}\right|_{I_{2i}=0}$$ (55)

In so far as the generator connected to port 1 is concerned, its load Z_L is the input impedance Z_{11} of port 1 when port 2 is terminated in R_{o2}. Then, from (7 and 10),

$$S_{11} = \frac{Z_{11} - R_{o1}}{Z_{11} + R_{o1}}$$ (56)

Therefore, the scattering parameter S_{11} is interpreted as the reflection coefficient at port 1 when port 2 is terminated in the reference resistance R_{o2}.

Similarly,

$$S_{22} = \left.\frac{b_2}{a_2}\right|_{a_1=0} = \left.\frac{\sqrt{R_{o2}}\, I_{2r}}{\sqrt{R_{o2}}\, I_{2i}}\right|_{I_{1i}=0} = \left.\frac{V_{2r}}{V_{2i}}\right|_{I_{1i}=0} = \frac{Z_{22} - R_{o2}}{Z_{22} + R_{o2}}$$ (57)

where Z_{22} is the input impedance of port 2 when port 1 is terminated in the reference resistance R_{o1}. Thus the scattering parameter S_{22} also represents a reflection coefficient under the conditions specified.

The evaluation of S_{21} proceeds in the same manner. Accordingly,

$$S_{21} = \left.\frac{b_2}{a_1}\right|_{a_2=0} = \left.\frac{\sqrt{R_{o2}}\, I_{2r}}{\sqrt{R_{o1}}\, I_{1i}}\right|_{I_{2i}=0}$$

$$= \frac{-\sqrt{R_{o2}}\, I_2}{\sqrt{R_{o1}}\, \dfrac{E_1}{2R_{o1}}} = -2\sqrt{R_{o1}}\,\sqrt{R_{o2}}\,\frac{I_2}{E_1}$$ (58)

Since $a_2 = 0$ when $E_2 = 0$ and $V_2 = -R_{o2}I_2$, then $V_2/\sqrt{R_{o2}} = -\sqrt{R_{o2}}\,I_2$. Therefore

$$S_{21} = 2\sqrt{\frac{R_{o1}}{R_{o2}}}\,\frac{V_2}{E_1} = \frac{V_2/\sqrt{R_{o2}}}{\frac{1}{2}E_1/\sqrt{R_{o1}}} \tag{59}$$

Equations (58) and (59) indicate that S_{21} represents a forward transmission coefficient from port 1 to port 2. It can be a complex number if V_2 and E_1 are out of phase as determined by the two-port network. Similarly,

$$S_{12} = \frac{b_1}{a_2}\bigg|_{a_1 = 0} = -2\sqrt{R_{o1}}\,\sqrt{R_{o2}}\,\frac{I_1}{E_2}$$

$$= 2\sqrt{\frac{R_{o2}}{R_{o1}}}\,\frac{V_1}{E_2} = \frac{V_1/\sqrt{R_{o1}}}{\frac{1}{2}E_2/\sqrt{R_{o2}}} \tag{60}$$

which indicates that S_{12} represents a reverse transmission coefficient from port 2 to port 1.

The scattering parameters for an n-port network can be determined in like manner. Consider, for example, one of the equations contained in (30) for a three-port network.

$$b_1 = S_{11}a_1 + S_{12}a_2 + S_{13}a_3$$

Then

$$S_{11} = \frac{b_1}{a_1}\bigg|_{a_2 = a_3 = 0} \tag{61}$$

which yields the reflection coefficient at port 1 when ports 2 and 3 are terminated in reference resistances R_{o2} and R_{o3} with $E_2 = E_3 = 0$. Also

$$S_{13} = \frac{b_1}{a_3}\bigg|_{a_1 = a_2 = 0} \tag{62}$$

which yields the transmission coefficient from port 3 to port 1 when ports 1 and 2 are terminated in reference resistances R_{o1} and R_{o2} with $E_1 = E_2 = 0$.

Example 6-3

Determine the scattering parameters for the tuned transformer shown in Fig. 6-5a. The primary and secondary circuits are individually series resonant at the frequency of operation. The coupling is adjusted for maximum power transfer. Assume

$$[R_o] = \begin{bmatrix} R_{o1} & 0 \\ 0 & R_{o2} \end{bmatrix}$$

Solution

Both S_{11} and S_{21} are determined from Fig. 6-5b in which $I_{2i} = 0$. Applying KVL to both loops

$$E_1 = I_1(R_{o1} - jX_{c_1} + jX_{L_1}) + j\omega M I_2 \tag{63}$$

$$0 = j\omega M I_1 + I_2(R_{o2} - jX_{c_2} + jX_{L_2}) \tag{64}$$

Solve (64) for I_2 and substitute into (63) to obtain

$$E_1 = I_1\left(R_{o1} - jX_{c_1} + jX_{L_1} + \frac{\omega^2 M^2}{R_{o2} - jX_{c_2} + jX_{L_2}}\right) \tag{65}$$

The last term in (65) represents the impedance reflected in series with the primary. Since each circuit individually is series resonant, (65) reduces to

$$E_1 = I_1\left(R_{o1} + \frac{\omega^2 M^2}{R_{o2}}\right) \tag{66}$$

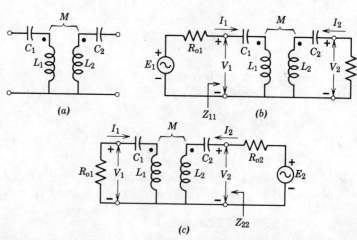

(a)

(b)

(c)

Figure 6-5. (a) Tuned transformer. (b) Circuit for determining S_{11} and S_{21}. (c) Circuit for determining S_{22} and S_{12}.

Maximum power transfer requires

$$\frac{\omega^2 M^2}{R_{o2}} = R_{o1}$$

or

$$\omega M = \sqrt{R_{o1}R_{o2}} \tag{67}$$

Since this makes $Z_{11} = R_{o1}$, then $V_{1r} = 0$ and $V_1 = V_{1i} = E_1/2$. Therefore, from (55) or (56), $S_{11} = 0$. The loop equations (63) and (64) become

$$E_1 = I_1 R_{o1} + j\sqrt{R_{o1}R_{o2}}\, I_2 \tag{68}$$

$$0 = j\sqrt{R_{o1}R_{o2}}\, I_1 + I_2 R_{o2} \tag{69}$$

To evaluate S_{21} using (58), solve (68) and (69) for I_2/E_1 to obtain

$$\frac{I_2}{E_1} = \frac{-j}{2\sqrt{R_{o1}R_{o2}}} \tag{70}$$

Therefore, from (58),

$$S_{21} = \frac{2j\sqrt{R_{o1}R_{o2}}}{2\sqrt{R_{o1}R_{o2}}} = j = 1\,\underline{/90°} \tag{71}$$

Both S_{22} and S_{12} are determined from Fig. 6-5c. Since $\omega M = \sqrt{R_{o1}R_{o2}}$, the loop equations are

$$0 = I_1 R_{o1} + j\sqrt{R_{o1}R_{o2}}\, I_2 \tag{72}$$

$$E_2 = j\sqrt{R_{o1}R_{o2}}\, I_1 + I_2 R_{o2} \tag{73}$$

Then, after eliminating I_1,

$$E_2 = I_2(R_{o2} + R_{o2}) \tag{74}$$

Since $Z_{22} = R_{o2}$, then $V_{2r} = 0$ and $V_2 = V_{2i} = E_2/2$. Therefore, from (57), $S_{22} = 0$. To evaluate S_{12} using (60), solve (72) and (73) for I_1/E_2 to obtain

$$\frac{I_1}{E_2} = \frac{-j}{2\sqrt{R_{o1}R_{o2}}} \tag{75}$$

Thus, from (60),

$$S_{12} = \frac{2j\sqrt{R_{o1}R_{o2}}}{2\sqrt{R_{o1}R_{o2}}} = j = 1\;\underline{/90^\circ} \tag{76}$$

6-5 PHYSICAL MEANINGS

Additional insight into the physical meanings of the normalized incident and reflected components and of the scattering parameters may be obtained by considering the augmented two-port network shown in Fig. 6-6a.

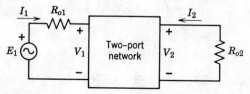

Figure 6-6(a). Augmented two-port network using reference resistances R_{o1} and R_{o2} with generator E_1.

From (46), $a_2 = 0$ since $V_2 = -R_{o2}I_2$. Using this in (52),

$$b_2 = \frac{V_2 - R_{o2}I_2}{2\sqrt{R_{o2}}} = \frac{-2R_{o2}I_2}{2\sqrt{R_{o2}}} = -\sqrt{R_{o2}}\,I_2 \tag{77}$$

Therefore,

$$|b_2|^2 = R_{o2}|I_2|^2 = \text{power } P_L \text{ delivered to } R_{o2}$$

Using (47) with the fact that $V_1 = E_1 - R_{o1}I_1$ from Fig. 6-6a yields

$$a_1 = \frac{E_1}{2\sqrt{R_{o1}}}$$

or

$$|a_1|^2 = \frac{|E_1|^2}{4R_{o1}} = \begin{array}{l}\text{power } P_A \text{ available from the} \\ \text{source with internal resistance } R_{o1}\end{array} \tag{78}$$

which is, by definition, the incident or matched power.

Rearrange (78) as

$$|a_1|^2 = \frac{E_1 E_1^*}{4R_{o1}} = \frac{1}{4R_{o1}}(V_1 + R_{o1}I_1)(V_1^* + R_{o1}I_1^*)$$

$$= \frac{1}{4R_{o1}}(|V_1|^2 + R_{o1}I_1 V_1^* + R_{o1}V_1 I_1^* + R_{o1}^2 |I_1|^2) \qquad (79)$$

Similarly, (51) yields

$$|b_1|^2 = \frac{1}{4R_{o1}}(V_1 - R_{o1}I_1)(V_1^* - R_{o1}I_1^*)$$

$$= \frac{1}{4R_{o1}}(|V_1|^2 - R_{o1}I_1 V_1^* - R_{o1}I_1^* V_1 + R_{o1}^2 |I_1|^2) \qquad (80)$$

Now subtract (80) from (79) to obtain

$$|a_1|^2 - |b_1|^2 = \frac{1}{4R_{o1}}(2R_{o1}I_1 V_1^* + 2R_{o1}I_1^* V_1)$$

$$= \tfrac{1}{2}(I_1 V_1^* + I_1^* V_1) = \operatorname{Re} I_1 V_1^* = \operatorname{Re} I_1^* V_1$$

$$= \text{power } P_1 \text{ delivered to port 1} \qquad (81)$$

Therefore,

$$|b_1|^2 = |a_1|^2 - P_1 = P_A - P_1$$

$$= \text{reflected or unmatched power from port 1} \qquad (82)$$

Since $a_2 = 0$ in Fig. 6-6a, then

$$|S_{11}|^2 = \frac{|b_1|^2}{|a_1|^2}\bigg|_{a_2=0} = \frac{P_A - P_1}{P_A} \qquad (83)$$

or

$$|S_{11}|^2 = \frac{\text{power reflected from port 1}}{\text{power available from the generator}} \qquad (84)$$

whereas S_{11} itself represents the reflection coefficient at port 1. If $|S_{11}| > 1$, the power reflected from port 1 is larger than the power available from the generator. This means that port 1 is a source of power. Also, from (58),

$$|S_{21}|^2 = \frac{|I_2|^2 R_{o2}}{|E_1|^2/4R_{o1}} = \frac{P_L}{P_A}$$

$$= \text{transducer power gain } G_T \qquad (85)$$

By connecting the generator and reference resistances as shown in Fig. 6-6b and by using similar procedures to those above, it can be shown that, since $a_1 = 0$,

$$|b_1|^2 = \text{power delivered to } R_{o1} \text{ from generator at port 2} \qquad (86)$$

$$|a_2|^2 = \text{power available from generator at port 2 with internal resistance } R_{o2}$$

$$\qquad (87)$$

$$|b_2|^2 = |a_2|^2 - \text{Re} \, I_2 V_2^* = |a_2|^2 - \text{Re} \, I_2^* V_2$$

$$= \text{reflected or unmatched power from port 2} \qquad (88)$$

and

$$|S_{22}|^2 = \frac{\text{power reflected from port 2}}{\text{power available from generator at port 2}} \qquad (89)$$

whereas S_{22} itself represents the reflection coefficient at port 2. If $|S_{22}| > 1$, port 2 is a source of power. Also, from (60),

$$|S_{12}|^2 = \frac{|I_1|^2 R_{o1}}{|E_2|^2/4R_{o2}}$$

$$= \text{reverse transducer power gain} \qquad (90)$$

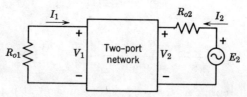

Figure 6-6(b). Augmented two-port network using reference resistances R_{o1} and R_{o2} with generator E_2.

The forward operating power gain is

$$G_p = \frac{\text{power } P_L \text{ delivered to } R_{o2}}{\text{power } P_1 \text{ delivered to port 1}}$$

$$= \frac{|b_2|^2}{|a_1|^2 - |b_1|^2}\bigg|_{a_2=0} = \frac{|b_2|^2/|a_1|^2}{1 - |b_1|^2/|a_1|^2}\bigg|_{a_2=0}$$

$$= \frac{|S_{21}|^2}{1 - |S_{11}|^2} \tag{91}$$

6-6 POTENTIAL INSTABILITY

The scattering parameters S_{11} and S_{22} represent reflection coefficients at the two ports. Thus,

$$S_{11} = \frac{Z_{11} - R_{o1}}{Z_{11} + R_{o1}} \quad \text{and} \quad S_{22} = \frac{Z_{22} - R_{o2}}{Z_{22} + R_{o2}}$$

Since the two expressions have the same form, consider

$$S = \frac{Z - R_o}{Z + R_o} \tag{92}$$

where $Z = R \pm jX$. Then

$$S = \frac{R \pm jX - R_o}{R \pm jX + R_o} \tag{93}$$

or

$$|S| = \frac{\sqrt{(R - R_o)^2 + X^2}}{\sqrt{(R + R_o)^2 + X^2}} \tag{94}$$

If $R > 0$, then $|S| < 1$, and if $R < 0$, then $|S| > 1$ (assuming that $R_o > 0$). It is important to observe from this that when $|S_{11}| > 1$, $Z_{11} = -R_{11} \pm jX_{11}$, and when $|S_{22}| > 1$, $Z_{22} = -R_{22} \pm jX_{22}$.

If the resistance at the terminals of the device is negative, the device is potentially unstable, and this condition is readily identified whenever $|S_{11}| > 1$ or $|S_{22}| > 1$. The circuit is usually stable whenever $|S_{11}| > 1$ and $|S_{22}| > 1$ and the reference resistance terminations are used.

It is also observed from (91) that the operating power gain becomes infinite when $|S_{11}| = 1$.

6-7 MEASUREMENT OF SCATTERING PARAMETERS

The basic relationships between the incident and reflected components, reference resistances, and the scattering parameters of a two-port device are summarized below.

$$b_1 = S_{11}a_1 + S_{12}a_2$$
$$b_2 = S_{21}a_1 + S_{22}a_2 \tag{95}$$

$$V_{1r} = R_{o1}I_{1r} \qquad V_{1i} = R_{o1}I_{1i}$$
$$V_{2r} = R_{o2}I_{2r} \qquad V_{2i} = R_{o2}I_{2i} \tag{96}$$

$$b_1 = \sqrt{R_{o1}}\, I_{1r} \qquad a_1 = \sqrt{R_{o1}}\, I_{1i}$$
$$b_2 = \sqrt{R_{o2}}\, I_{2r} \qquad a_2 = \sqrt{R_{o2}}\, I_{2i} \tag{97}$$

Substituting (97) into (95) yields

$$\sqrt{R_{o1}}\, I_{1r} = S_{11}\sqrt{R_{o1}}\, I_{1i} + S_{12}\sqrt{R_{o2}}\, I_{2i}$$

$$\tag{98}$$

$$\sqrt{R_{o2}}\, I_{2r} = S_{21}\sqrt{R_{o2}}\, I_{1i} + S_{22}\sqrt{R_{o2}}\, I_{2i}$$

If the two reference resistances are equal, that is, $R_{o1} = R_{o2} = R_o$, then (98) becomes

$$I_{1r} = S_{11}I_{1i} + S_{12}I_{2i}$$
$$I_{2r} = S_{21}I_{1i} + S_{22}I_{2i} \tag{99}$$

Also, using (96) in (99) with equal reference resistances yields

$$V_{1r} = S_{11}V_{1i} + S_{12}V_{2i}$$
$$V_{2r} = S_{21}V_{1i} + S_{22}V_{2i} \tag{100}$$

Thus, for the important special case where $R_{o1} = R_{o2} = R_o$, the scattering parameters can be directly determined from measurements of the incident and reflected voltages using commercially available directional couplers and a voltmeter-phasemeter instrument. Hence, from (100),

$$S_{11} = \frac{V_{1r}}{V_{1i}}\bigg|_{V_{2i}=0} \qquad S_{12} = \frac{V_{1r}}{V_{2i}}\bigg|_{V_{1i}=0}$$

$$S_{21} = \frac{V_{2r}}{V_{1i}}\bigg|_{V_{2i}=0} \qquad S_{22} = \frac{V_{2r}}{V_{2i}}\bigg|_{V_{1i}=0} \tag{101}$$

When measurements are to be made, the network or device whose scattering parameters are to be determined is mounted in a special jig. A signal source whose internal resistance is $R_o = 50\ \Omega$ is connected via 50-Ω transmission lines to the input port through an input directional coupler, and the output port is connected via 50-Ω lines to a 50-Ω load through an output directional coupler. After any necessary initial calibration steps and bias settings are performed, the equipment measures the desired incident and reflected component magnitudes and phase angles. Since $V_{2i} = 0$ in this situation, S_{11} and S_{21} are determined. The process is then repeated with the jig reversed to make $V_{1i} = 0$, and S_{12} and S_{22} are determined.

The scattering parameters depend upon the type of network or device and its operating conditions, temperature, and frequency of the signal source. Typical values for a certain transistor at a single frequency and temperature are

$$S_{11} = 0.68\ \underline{/-42^\circ} \qquad S_{12} = 0.015\ \underline{/85^\circ}$$

$$S_{21} = 4.1\ \underline{/108^\circ} \qquad S_{22} = 0.90\ \underline{/-9^\circ}$$

Similarly, for a three-port device using equal reference resistances at all three ports, (99) and (100) become

$$I_{1r} = S_{11}I_{1i} + S_{12}I_{2i} + S_{13}I_{3i}$$

$$I_{2r} = S_{21}I_{1i} + S_{22}I_{2i} + S_{23}I_{3i} \tag{102}$$

$$I_{3r} = S_{31}I_{1i} + S_{32}I_{2i} + S_{33}I_{3i}$$

and

$$V_{1r} = S_{11}V_{1i} + S_{12}V_{2i} + S_{13}V_{3i}$$

$$V_{2r} = S_{21}V_{1i} + S_{22}V_{2i} + S_{23}V_{3i} \tag{103}$$

$$V_{3r} = S_{31}V_{1i} + S_{32}V_{2i} + S_{33}V_{3i}$$

Thus

$$S_{11} = \left. \frac{V_{1r}}{V_{1i}} \right|_{V_{2i} = V_{3i} = 0} \qquad S_{12} = \left. \frac{V_{1r}}{V_{2i}} \right|_{V_{1i} = V_{3i} = 0} \qquad (104)$$

$$S_{31} = \left. \frac{V_{3r}}{V_{1i}} \right|_{V_{2i} = V_{3i} = 0} \qquad S_{33} = \left. \frac{V_{3r}}{V_{3i}} \right|_{V_{1i} = V_{2i} = 0}$$

Incident voltages at the ports to which no generator is connected are automatically equal to zero because of the reference resistances used as the terminations.

An important aspect of measuring scattering parameters of a transistor should be mentioned. The transistor can be considered to be a two-port device as shown in Fig. 6-7a or as a three-port as in Fig. 6-7b.

When S_{11} is measured for the grounded-emitter circuit of Fig. 6-7a using reference 50-Ω resistances, a different value is obtained than when S_{11} is measured for the circuit of Fig. 6-7b. This is because the emitter is not grounded in Fig. 6-7b but has the reference 50-Ω terminating resistance in

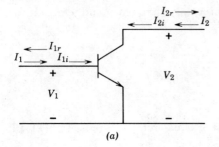

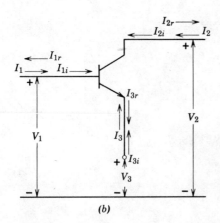

Figure 6-7. (a) A transistor considered as a two-port device. (b) A transistor considered as a three-port device.

series with the emitter lead. It is expected that S_{12}, S_{21}, and S_{22} for the two circuits will be different for similar reasons.

The manufacturer's specifications as given on the device's data sheets must give the reference resistances used, and whether the scattering parameters specified are for the device considered as a two-port or as a three-port arrangement. Special attention is required to convert from three-port to two-port scattering parameters.

6-71 Directional Couplers

Directional couplers and short lengths of coaxial transmission lines are inserted into lumped constant systems whose scattering parameters are to be determined. When a transmission line is not terminated properly, reflected voltage, current, and power exist in addition to incident components. The directional coupler is a device that provides an output voltage proportional to either the reflected component or the incident component, depending on the way it is inserted into the circuit.

The directional coupler shown in Fig. 6-8a is composed of a short length of coaxial line with a loop coupled to the inner conductor. It operates by virtue of the capacitive and mutual inductive coupling between the loop and

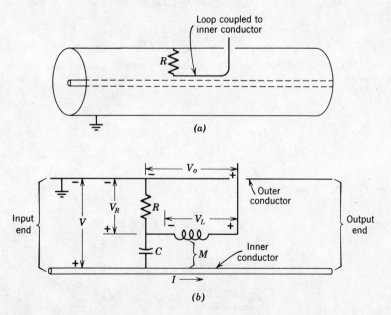

Figure 6-8.   *(a) Construction of one type of directional coupler. (b) Simplified circuit showing capacitive and mutual inductive coupling between the loop and inner conductor.*

inner conductor. A simplified circuit is shown in Fig. 6-8b. The series RC combination acts as a voltage divider. Thus,

$$V_R = V\frac{R}{R + \dfrac{1}{j\omega C}} \tag{105}$$

If $R \ll 1/j\omega C$, (105) becomes

$$V_R \cong j\omega C R V \tag{106}$$

Current I in the inner conductor induces V_L in the loop. Thus,

$$V_L \cong -j\omega M I \tag{107}$$

The output voltage is

$$V_o = V_R + V_L = j\omega C R V - j\omega M I \tag{108}$$

If the coupler is designed such that

$$CR = \frac{M}{R_o} \tag{109}$$

where R_o = characteristic resistance of the coaxial line, then (108) becomes

$$V_o = j\omega M \left(\frac{V}{R_o} - I \right) \tag{110}$$

The voltage and current decomposition equations are

$$V = V_i + V_r \tag{111}$$

and

$$I = I_i - I_r = \frac{V_i}{R_o} - \frac{V_r}{R_o} \tag{112}$$

Thus (110) becomes

$$V_o = j\omega M \left(\frac{V_i + V_r}{R_o} - I_i + I_r \right)$$

$$= j\omega M (I_i + I_r - I_i + I_r)$$

$$= j\omega M 2 I_r \tag{113}$$

Therefore the output voltage is proportional to the reflected current (or voltage) because the incident components cancel when the coupler is connected as shown in Fig. 6-8b. If the coupler is reversed, its output voltage is proportional to the incident current and the reflected components cancel.

In practice, the directional effect is not perfect, with directivities of about 30 dB being typical. The output voltage is usually rectified and filtered to drive a DC meter.

6-8 INDEFINITE SCATTERING MATRIX

The transistor in Fig. 6-7b "floats" relative to the common ground or reference connection. Each of the three terminals of the device is paired with the reference ground to form a port. The scattering parameters for this three-port arrangement are independent of transistor orientation. The matrix thus formed is an indefinite scattering matrix because no definite choice has been made to ground any particular transistor terminal. Thus

$$b_1 = S_{11}a_1 + S_{12}a_2 + S_{13}a_3$$

$$b_2 = S_{21}a_1 + S_{22}a_2 + S_{23}a_3 \tag{114}$$

$$b_3 = S_{31}a_1 + S_{32}a_2 + S_{33}a_3$$

The important properties of the indefinite scattering matrix are that the sum of any row and of any column equals unity. This is comparable to the indefinite admittance matrix in which the sum of any row and of any column equals zero.

That the sum of any column of the indefinite scattering matrix equals unity can be proved readily by applying Kirchoff's current law to point P in Fig. 6-9a. Since ports 2 and 3 are terminated in the reference resistance R_o and since $E_2 = E_3 = 0$, the incident components at both ports equal zero, or $I_{2i} = I_{3i} = 0$ and $a_2 = a_3 = 0$. Thus, at P,

$$I_{1r} - I_{1i} + I_{2r} + I_{3r} = 0$$

or

$$I_{1i} = I_{1r} + I_{2r} + I_{3r} \tag{115}$$

Then (114) becomes

$$b_1 = S_{11}a_1$$

$$b_2 = S_{21}a_1 \tag{116}$$

$$b_3 = S_{31}a_1$$

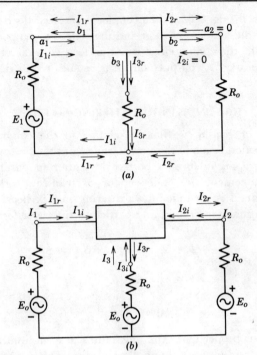

Figure 6-9. *Circuits used to extablish that the sum of any column (a) or of any row (b) in the indefinite scattering matrix equals unity.*

or

$$\sqrt{R_o}\, I_{1r} = S_{11} \sqrt{R_o}\, I_{1i}$$

$$\sqrt{R_o}\, I_{2r} = S_{21} \sqrt{R_o}\, I_{1i} \tag{117}$$

$$\sqrt{R_o}\, I_{3r} = S_{31} \sqrt{R_o}\, I_{1i}$$

Cancelling out R_o, adding, and using (115) yields

$$S_{11} + S_{21} + S_{31} = \frac{I_{1r} + I_{2r} + I_{3r}}{I_{1i}} = 1 \tag{118}$$

By using the generator E_2 and then E_3 with the other ports terminated in R_o, a similar procedure shows that $S_{12} + S_{22} + S_{32} = 1$ and $S_{13} + S_{23} + S_{33} = 1$. Thus the sum of any column equals unity.

In Fig. 6-9b, all generators are set equal to E_o. Since all three terminals of the device are raised the same voltage, the currents I_1, I_2, and I_3 each equals zero. Thus $I_{1i} = I_{1r}$, $I_{2i} = I_{2r}$, $I_{3i} = I_{3r}$. In addition, the incident currents at all three ports are equal, or $I_{1i} = I_{2i} = I_{3i}$, because the generators are identical. Substituting into the first row of (114)

$$b_1 = S_{11}a_1 + S_{12}a_2 + S_{13}a_3$$

gives

$$\sqrt{R_o}\, I_{1r} = S_{11}\sqrt{R_o}\, I_{1i} + S_{12}\sqrt{R_o}\, I_{2i} + S_{13}\sqrt{R_o}\, I_{3i}$$

or

$$I_{1r} = (S_{11} + S_{12} + S_{13})I_{1i} \tag{119}$$

However, since $I_{1i} = I_{1r}$, this becomes

$$S_{11} + S_{12} + S_{13} = 1 \tag{120}$$

A similar procedure applied to the second and third rows of (114) shows that $S_{21} + S_{22} + S_{23} = 1$ and $S_{31} + S_{32} + S_{33} = 1$.

There are only four independent scattering parameters in the nine elements of the matrix for a three-port device. All the others can then be calculated to complete the indefinite scattering matrix. Which four are to be considered independent is probably best determined by the relative ease of measuring the individual parameters. Forward-direction transmission coefficients are generally easier to measure than reverse direction transmission coefficients. Of course, only two parameters in any row or column are independent. It is best to arrange the elements in rows and columns according to the sequence base, emitter, collector.

6-9 ACTIVITY AND PASSIVITY

From (81), the average power delivered to port 1 is

$$P_1 = |a_1|^2 - |b_1|^2 = a_1^* a_1 - b_1^* b_1 \tag{121}$$

Similarly, the average power delivered to port i of an n-port network is

$$P_i = |a_i|^2 - |b_i|^2 = a_i^* a_i - b_i^* b_i \tag{122}$$

The total power delivered to all n ports is given by

$$P = [a^*]^t [a] - [b^*]^t [b] \tag{123}$$

where $[a]$ and $[b]$ are column matrices representing the incident and reflected components at the n ports.

Since

$$[b] = [S][a] \tag{124}$$

and

$$[b*]^t = ([S*][a*])^t = [a*]^t[S*]^t \tag{125}$$

then, substituting (124) and (125) into (123),

$$P = [a*]^t[a] - [a*]^t[S*]^t[S][a] \tag{126}$$

or, factoring,

$$P = [a*]^t([I] - [S*]^t[S])[a] \tag{127}$$

where [I] is the unit diagonal matrix.

The dissipation matrix $([I] - [S*]^t[S])$ is always hermitian, so that (127) is the hermitian form for the power P (see Section 1-4). For passivity, the power $P \geqslant 0$ for all $a \neq 0$, so that the hermitian form is positive-semidefinite. This means that the determinant of the dissipation matrix and that of its principal minors must be nonnegative for passivity.

In terms of the two-port scattering parameters, the dissipation matrix becomes

$$([I] - [S*]^t[S]) = \begin{bmatrix} 1 - |S_{11}|^2 - |S_{21}|^2 & S_{11}^*S_{12} + S_{21}^*S_{22} \\ S_{11}S_{12}^* + S_{21}S_{22}^* & 1 - |S_{22}|^2 - |S_{12}|^2 \end{bmatrix} \tag{128}$$

This is indeed hermitian since elements on the principal diagonal are real and elements symmetrically located relative to the principal diagonal are complex conjugates. Hence, for passivity,

$$|S_{11}|^2 + |S_{21}|^2 < 1 \tag{129}$$

and

$$|S_{11}|^2 + |S_{21}|^2 + |S_{22}|^2 + |S_{12}|^2 - |D|^2 < 1 \tag{130}$$

where

$$D = S_{11}S_{22} - S_{12}S_{21}$$

Interchanging the input and output ports also indicates that, for passivity,

$$|S_{22}|^2 + |S_{12}|^2 < 1 \tag{131}$$

If any one of the above passivity conditions is violated, the circuit is active.

The two-port circuit is lossless if each of the elements in the dissipation matrix (128) equals zero. This leads to $|S_{11}| = |S_{22}|$ and $|S_{12}| = |S_{21}|$ (Problem 6-9).

PROBLEMS

6-1. Given the two-port z parameters z_i, z_r, z_f, z_o, and unequal reference-resistance terminations R_{o1} and R_{o2}.

(a) Use (25) to determine the normalized scattering parameters in terms of the normalized z parameters defined as

$$[z'] = \begin{bmatrix} \dfrac{z_i}{R_{o1}} & \dfrac{z_r}{\sqrt{R_{o1}R_{o2}}} \\[3ex] \dfrac{z_f}{\sqrt{R_{o1}R_{o2}}} & \dfrac{z_o}{R_{o2}} \end{bmatrix}$$

(Note: normalize the parameters in the last step.)

(b) Rewrite the results of (a) if $R_{o1} = R_{o2} = R_o$ and compare to a table of conversions.

6-2. Given the two-port y parameters y_i, y_r, y_f, y_o, and unequal reference-resistance terminations R_{o1} and R_{o2}.

(a) Use (25) to determine the normalized scattering parameters in terms of the normalized y parameters defined as

$$[y'] = \begin{bmatrix} y_i\sqrt{R_{o1}} & y_r\sqrt{R_{o1}R_{o2}} \\[2ex] y_f\sqrt{R_{o1}R_{o2}} & y_oR_{o2} \end{bmatrix}$$

(Note: Normalize the y parameters in the last step.)

(b) Rewrite the results of (a) if $R_{o1} = R_{o2} = R_o$ and compare to a table of conversions.

6-3. Given the y parameter equivalent circuit and unequal reference-resistance terminations R_{o1} and R_{o2}:

(a) Use (56) to determine S_{11}.

(b) Use (57) to determine S_{22}.

(c) Use (59) to determine S_{21}.

(d) Use (60) to determine S_{12}.

To obtain the final result in all cases, normalize the y parameters and compare to the results of Problem 6-2.

6-4. Repeat the calculations of Problem 6-3 for h parameters instead of y parameters. Determine whether or not the normalized h parameters can be defined as

$$[h'] = \begin{bmatrix} R_{o1}h_i & h_r\sqrt{\dfrac{R_{o1}}{R_{o2}}} \\ h_f\sqrt{\dfrac{R_{o1}}{R_{o2}}} & \dfrac{h_o}{R_{o2}} \end{bmatrix}$$

6-5. The h parameters are related to terminal voltages and currents by

$$V_1 = h_i I_1 + h_r V_2$$

$$I_2 = h_f I_1 + h_o V_2$$

Substitute (46), (47), (51), and (52) into (39) and (40) in order to also relate the scattering parameters to terminal voltages and currents. Solve these latter relationships for the h parameters in terms of the scattering parameters.

6-6. A transistor has $S_{11} = 0.8 + j0.8$.
 (a) Is the transistor inherently stable? Why?
 (b) How would you locate this "reflection coefficient" on the Smith chart?
 (c) If $R_{o1} = R_{o2} = 50\ \Omega$, what is the input impedance of the transistor for the specified value of S_{11}?

6-7. The CE scattering parameters of a transistor are

$$S_{11} = 0.505 - j0.455 = 0.68\ \underline{/-42°}$$

$$S_{12} = 0.0149 + j0.00131 = 0.015\ \underline{/5°}$$

$$S_{21} = -1.27 + j3.9 = 4.1\ \underline{/108°}$$

$$S_{22} = 0.888 - j0.141 = 0.9\ \underline{/-9°}$$

 (a) Determine the CB and CC scattering parameters.
 (b) Is the device active or passive in each of the three configurations?
 (c) If $R_{o1} = R_{o2} = 50\ \Omega$, calculate the CE y parameters.

6-8. Determine whether the linear circuits with normalized scattering parameters as given below are active or passive and determine which are lossless.

(a) $[S] = \frac{1}{3}\begin{bmatrix} -1 & 2 & 2 \\ 2 & -1 & 2 \\ 2 & 2 & -1 \end{bmatrix}$ (b) $[S] = \frac{1}{2}\begin{bmatrix} 0 & -1 & 1 \\ -1 & 1 & 1 \\ 1 & 0 & 1 \end{bmatrix}$

(c) $[S] = \frac{1}{3}\begin{bmatrix} 0 & 1 & 2 \\ 1 & 0 & 1 \\ 2 & 1 & 0 \end{bmatrix}$

6-9. Show that if a two-port circuit is lossless, then

$$|S_{11}| = |S_{22}| \quad \text{and} \quad |S_{12}| = |S_{21}|.$$

6-10.
(a) Given $[I] = [y][V]$ and $[b] = [S][a]$. Substitute for $[a]$ from (48) and substitute for $[b]$ from (53). Eliminate the current matrix and solve for $[y]$ to show that

$$[y] = [R_o]^{-1/2}([S] + [I])^{-1}([I] - [S])[R_o]^{-1/2}$$

in which [I] is the unit diagonal matrix.
(b) Given $[V] = [z][I]$. Repeat the substitutions of (a) and show that

$$[z] = [R_o]^{1/2}([I] - [S])^{-1}([S] + [I])[R_o]^{-1/2}[R_o].$$

6-11. Determine S_{11} for the circuit shown in Fig. 6-10 when the coupling is adjusted such that the primary is series resonant.

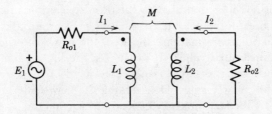

Figure 6-10. Circuit for Problem 6-11.

CHAPTER SEVEN

DESIGN USING SCATTERING PARAMETERS

7-0 INTRODUCTION

Broadband measurements of scattering parameters of transistors are usually referred to the 50-Ω characteristic resistance of the coaxial interconnections, so that $R_{o1} = R_{o2} = 50\Omega$. If the transistor is then used in an amplifier circuit where the source and load terminations for the transistor are both equal to 50Ω, the forward operating power gain is given directly by 6-91 as

$$G_p = \frac{|S_{21}|^2}{1 - |S_{11}|^2} \tag{1}$$

and the transducer power gain is given by 6-85 as

$$G_T = |S_{21}|^2 \tag{2}$$

where the scattering parameters are measured values.

However it is not often desirable for the transistor terminations to be 50 Ω. Other criteria need to be considered, such as power gain and bandwidth.

If other than 50-Ω terminations are used, the new scattering parameters differ from the measured values. If the new scattering parameters could be determined, then their use in (1) and (2) instead of the measured values gives the resulting power gains. Determining the new scattering parameters is complicated by the fact that they depend not only on the transistor and its operating conditions, but also on the terminations. The new parameters cannot be measured because the measurement system usually requires 50-Ω terminations. Therefore the new scattering parameters must be calculated in terms of the measured scattering parameters and arbitrary terminating impedances for the transistor.

7-1 CALCULATION OF GENERALIZED SCATTERING PARAMETERS

A procedure that will provide the desired relationships is outlined in steps as follows.

Step 1.   Convert the original measured scattering parameters for the 50-Ω terminations into z parameters. This is done because z parameters are independent of the terminating impedances provided the operating conditions of the transistor are maintained constant. Of course, either the y or h parameters could be used instead.

Step 2.   Express the new scattering parameters in terms of z parameters and arbitrary terminating impedances. This is done independently of step 1 in order to relate the new scattering parameters to arbitrary terminations. Unfortunately, the z parameters are also involved in the expressions, but they are only "excess baggage" and should be eliminated.

Step 3. Eliminate the z parameters from the relationship obtained in step 2 by substituting the z parameters from step 1. The resulting expression relates the new scattering parameters to the arbitrary terminating impedances and the measured scattering parameters.

Although it is easy to state the above procedure in words, the actual step-by-step manipulations become involved, tedious, and tricky. The serious student, however, is generally curious about such derivations. Therefore, to serve his purposes, the material in Appendix A leads around the otherwise frustrating errors and omissions in the pertinent literature and provides an available reference to which the student can turn for details of the derivation.

The result obtained in Appendix A expresses the new or generalized scattering parameters $[S']$ in terms of the arbitrary terminating impedances Z_i and the measured scattering parameters $[S]$ as

$$[S'] = [A]^{-1}([S] - [r^*])([I] - [r][S])^{-1}[A^*] \qquad (3)$$

where

$$A_i = (1 - r_i^*)\frac{\sqrt{1 - |r_i|^2}}{|1 - r_i|}$$

= the iith element of the diagonal

matrix corresponding to the ith port   (4)

$$r_i = \frac{Z_i - R_o}{Z_i + R_o}$$

= the iith element of the diagonal

reflection-coefficient matrix

corresponding to the ith port   (5)

Z_i = the arbitrary terminating impedance

of the ith port

and I is the unit diagonal matrix. Equation 3 is valid for an n-port network. If the transistor is considered as a two-port network and if it is to be operated with terminating impedances Z_1 and Z_2 at the input and output ports respectively, (3) expands to give the generalized scattering parameters as

$$S'_{11} = \frac{A_1^*}{A_1} \frac{[(1 - r_2 S_{22})(S_{11} - r_1^*) + r_2 S_{12} S_{21}]}{[(1 - r_1 S_{11})(1 - r_2 S_{22}) - r_1 r_2 S_{12} S_{21}]} \qquad (6)$$

$$S'_{12} = \frac{A_2^*}{A_1} \frac{S_{12}(1 - |r_1|^2)}{[(1 - r_1 S_{11})(1 - r_2 S_{22}) - r_1 r_2 S_{12} S_{21}]} \qquad (7)$$

$$S'_{21} = \frac{A_1^*}{A_2} \frac{S_{21}(1 - |r_2|^2)}{[(1 - r_1 S_{11})(1 - r_2 S_{22}) - r_1 r_2 S_{12} S_{21}]} \qquad (8)$$

$$S'_{22} = \frac{A_2^*}{A_2} \frac{[(1 - r_1 S_{11})(S_{22} - r_2^*) + r_1 S_{12} S_{21}]}{[(1 - r_1 S_{11})(1 - r_2 S_{22}) - r_1 r_2 S_{12} S_{21}]} \qquad (9)$$

in which the A_i and A_i^* are found from (4) and the r_i and r_i^* are found from (5).

The expressions (6), (7), (8), and (9) for the generalized scattering parameters simplify to the measured parameters if the terminations Z_i equal R_o, because the reflection coefficients given by (5) become zero.

When arbitrary terminations are used, the operating power gain is

$$G'_p = \frac{|S'_{21}|^2}{1 - |S'_{11}|^2} \qquad (10)$$

and the transducer power gain is

$$G'_T = |S'_{21}|^2 \qquad (11)$$

7-2 THE UNILATERAL AMPLIFIER

When the scattering parameter S_{12} is sufficiently small to neglect completely, the device is unilateral because there is no internal feedback. The generalized scattering parameters for this unilateral device are found from (6), (7), (8), and (9) by setting $S_{12}=0$. Thus

$$S'_{11,u} = \frac{A_1^*}{A_1}\left(\frac{S_{11}-r_1^*}{1-r_1 S_{11}}\right) = \frac{1-r_1}{1-r_1^*}\frac{S_{11}-r_1^*}{1-r_1 S_{11}} \tag{12}$$

$$S'_{12,u} = 0 \tag{13}$$

$$S'_{21,u} = \frac{A_1^*}{A_2}\frac{S_{21}(1-|r_2|^2)}{(1-r_1 S_{11})(1-r_2 S_{22})} \tag{14}$$

$$S'_{22,u} = \frac{A_2^*}{A_2}\left(\frac{S_{22}-r_2^*}{1-r_2 S_{22}}\right) = \frac{1-r_2}{1-r_2^*}\frac{S_{22}-r_2^*}{1-r_2 S_{22}} \tag{15}$$

The unilateral operating power gain becomes

$$(G'_p)_u = \frac{|S'_{21,u}|^2}{1-|S'_{11,u}|^2}$$

$$= |S_{21}|^2 \frac{1-|r_1|^2}{|1-r_1 S_{11}|^2-|S_{11}-r_1^*|^2}\cdot\frac{1-|r_2|^2}{|1-r_2 S_{22}|^2} \tag{16}$$

The second factor in (16) that involves r_1 can be simplified. Since r_1 and S_{11} are both complex numbers, let $r_1 = U_1 + jV_1$ and $S_{11} = A_{11} + jB_{11}$. After performing the manipulations, the second factor is found to be equivalent to

$$\frac{1}{1-|S_{11}|^2}$$

Thus (16) becomes

$$(G'_p)_u = \frac{|S_{21}|^2}{1-|S_{11}|^2}\cdot\frac{1-|r_2|^2}{|1-r_2 S_{22}|^2}$$

$$= G_p\frac{1-|r_2|^2}{|1-r_2 S_{22}|^2} \tag{17}$$

where $G_p = |S_{21}|^2/(1-|S_{11}|^2)$ represents the operating power gain with 50-Ω terminations. Notice that the unilateral operating power gain of (17) is independent of r_1 but depends upon r_2 and, therefore, the load impedance. In (17), the factor defined as

$$G_2 = \frac{1 - |r_2|^2}{|1 - r_2 S_{22}|^2} \qquad (18)$$

indicates any additional power gain or loss obtained by changing the load impedance from R_o to Z_2.

Unilateral operating power gain is maximized (assuming inherent stability) when there is a conjugate match at the output port. This means that

$$r_2 = S_{22}^* \qquad (19)$$

Therefore the maximum unilateral operating power gain is, from (17),

$$G_u = \frac{|S_{21}|^2}{(1 - |S_{11}|^2)(1 - |S_{22}|^2)} \qquad (20)$$

The unilateral transducer power gain becomes

$$(G_T')_u = |S_{21,u}'|^2 = |S_{21}|^2 \frac{|1 - |r_1|^2|}{|1 - r_1 S_{11}|^2} \cdot \frac{|1 - |r_2|^2|}{|1 - r_2 S_{22}|^2}$$

$$= G_T G_1 G_2 \qquad (21)$$

where $G_T = |S_{21}|^2$ represents transducer power gain with 50-Ω terminations and

$$G_i = \frac{|1 - |r_i|^2|}{|1 - r_i S_{ii}|^2} \qquad i = 1, 2 \qquad (22)$$

indicates any additional power gain or loss obtained by changing the source and load impedances to Z_1 and Z_2.

Assuming inherent stability, G_1 is maximized when

$$r_1 = S_{11}^* \qquad (23)$$

and G_2 is maximized when

$$r_2 = S_{22}^* \qquad (24)$$

or, in other words, a conjugate match exists at each port. Therefore, the maximum unilateral transducer power gain is, from (21),

$$G_u = \frac{|S_{21}|^2}{|1 - |S_{11}|^2 \cdot |1 - |S_{22}|^2|} \qquad (25)$$

This is the same as the maximum unilateral operating power gain and maximum unilateral available gain.

The value of G_u is finite for inherent stability. For the unilateral amplifier, this requires that $|S_{11}| < 1$ and $|S_{22}| < 1$.

The source and load impedances required to obtain G_u may be determined conveniently from the Smith chart. First, locate $r_i = S_{ii}^*$. If S_{ii}^* is given in polar form, use the "angle of reflection coefficient" scale and find the magnitude distance using the linear radial scale. If S_{ii}^* is given in rectangular form, use the linear radial scale to find the magnitudes of the distances corresponding to the real and imaginary parts of S_{ii}. Then, after locating $r_i = S_{ii}^*$, for $i = 1$ and 2, the normalized values of the Smith chart circles passing through the points r_i are equal to Z_i / R_o.

For conditions other than conjugate matching, the unilateral power gains depend upon how G_i behaves as the source and load impedances are changed. This behavior can be determined by examining

$$G_i = \frac{|1 - |r_i|^2|}{|1 - r_i S_{ii}|^2} \tag{26}$$

when G_i is assumed constant.

Two cases arise: case A for which $|S_{ii}| < 1$ and case B for which $|S_{ii}| > 1$.

7.21 Case A: $|S_{ii}| < 1$

The value of G_i in (22) is maximized when $r_i = S_{ii}^*$. Thus

$$G_{i,\max} = \frac{1}{1 - |S_{ii}|^2} \tag{27}$$

It is helpful to define a normalized gain factor as

$$g_i = \frac{G_i}{G_{i,\max}} = G_i(1 - |S_{ii}|^2) = \frac{|1 - |r_i|^2|}{|1 - r_i S_{ii}|^2}(1 - |S_{ii}|^2) \tag{28}$$

and for which $0 < g_i < 1$. The object now is to determine values of r_i for which g_i is constant using a transistor with specified S_{ii}.

Let

$$r_i = U_i + jV_i \tag{29}$$

and

$$S_{ii} = A_{ii} + jB_{ii} \tag{30}$$

Since r_i represents reflection coefficients, then U_i and jV_i represent the (discarded) axes of the Smith chart. Substitute (29) and (30) into (28). After performing the required manipulations, the result can be written as

$$\left[U_i - \frac{g_i A_{ii}}{1 - |S_{ii}|^2 (1 - g_i)} \right]^2 + \left[V_i + \frac{g_i B_{ii}}{1 - |S_{ii}|^2 (1 - g_i)} \right]^2 = \left[\frac{\sqrt{1 - g_i} \, (1 - |S_{ii}|^2)}{1 - |S_{ii}|^2 (1 - g_i)} \right]^2$$

$$(31)$$

This represents a family of circles in which normalized power gain g_i is a parameter. The centers of the circles are located at

$$U_c = \frac{g_i A_{ii}}{1 - |S_{ii}|^2 (1 - g_i)} \tag{32}$$

$$V_c = - \frac{g_i B_{ii}}{1 - |S_{ii}|^2 (1 - g_i)} \tag{33}$$

as illustrated in Fig. 7-1.

It is also seen that

$$\tan \alpha_i = \frac{-B_{ii}}{A_{ii}} \tag{34}$$

This means that the centers are located along a line between the origin of the Smith chart and a point for which the real part is A_{ii} and the imaginary

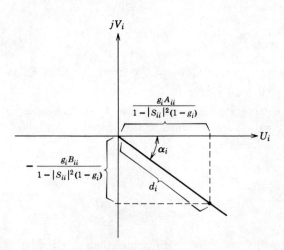

Figure 7-1.   Location of the constant-power-gain-circle centers.

part is $-B_{ii}$. This point, of course, is S_{ii}^*, for which maximum unilateral operating power gain is obtained.

The distance d_i along this line from the chart origin to the center of a constant-power-gain circle is given by the square root of the sum of squares of (32) and (33). The result is

$$d_i = \frac{g_i|S_{ii}|}{1-|S_{ii}|^2(1-g_i)} \tag{35}$$

From (31), the radius of a circle is

$$\rho_i = \frac{\sqrt{1-g_i}\,(1-|S_{ii}|^2)}{1-|S_{ii}|^2(1-g_i)} \tag{36}$$

The radius is zero for $G_i = G_{i,\max}$, or $g_i = 1$, so that power-gain circle is only a point at S_{ii}^*.

If 50-Ω terminations are used, then $r_i = 0$ and $G_i = 1$ (or 0 dB). This gives, from (28),

$$g_i = 1-|S_{ii}|^2 \qquad \text{for } G_i = 1 \tag{37}$$

Substituting this into (35) and (36) results in equal values for d_i and radius ρ_i. Thus

$$d_i = \rho_i = \frac{|S_{ii}|}{1+|S_{ii}|^2} \qquad \text{for } G_i = 1 \tag{38}$$

This means that the 0-dB circle for G_i passes through the origin of the Smith chart. Inside this particular circle $G_i > 1$, and this region indicates the values of Z_i/R_o for which the power gain is higher than for the 50-Ω termination. Outside this particular circle, $G_i < 1$.

Example 7-1.

The scattering parameters of a transistor at 500 MHz in a 50-Ω system are

$$S_{11} = 0.8 \,\underline{/-80^\circ} \qquad S_{12} \cong 0$$

$$S_{22} = 0.8 \,\underline{/-80^\circ} \qquad |S_{21}| \cong 2$$

Determine (a) Maximum power gain, (b) optimum terminations, (c) several power-gain circles.

Solution

(a) $G_T = |S_{21}|^2 = 4 = 6$ dB

$$G_{1,max} = \frac{1}{1 - |S_{11}|^2} = \frac{1}{1 - 0.64} = 2.78 = 4.4 \text{ dB}$$

$$G_{2,max} = \frac{1}{1 - |S_{22}|^2} = \frac{1}{1 - 0.64} = 2.78 = 4.4 \text{ dB}$$

The maximum power gain is

$$G_u = 4 \times 2.78 \times 2.78 = 30.91 = 14.8 \text{ dB}$$

(b) Maximum power gain is obtained with a conjugate match at both ports. Thus $r_1 = S_{11}^* = 0.8 \; \underline{/+80°}$ and $r_2 = S_{22}^* = 0.8 \; \underline{/+80°}$. From the Smith chart, this reflection coefficient yields

$$\frac{Z_{s1}}{50} = \frac{Z_{s2}}{50} = 0.26 + j1.16$$

so

$$Z_{s1} = Z_{s2} = 13 + j58 \; \Omega$$

(c) For $G_1 = 1 = 0$ dB; $g_1 = G_1(1 - |S_{11}|^2 = 1(1 - 0.64) = 0.36$

$$d_1 = \frac{g_1 |S_{11}|}{1 - |S_{11}|^2(1 - g_1)} = \frac{0.36(0.8)}{1 - 0.64(1 - 0.36)} = \frac{0.288}{0.59} = 0.49$$

$$\rho_1 = \frac{\sqrt{1 - g_1} \; (1 - |S_{11}|^2)}{1 - |S_{11}|^2(1 - g_1)} = \frac{\sqrt{1 - 0.36} \; (1 - 0.64)}{0.59} = 0.49$$

Other values for the circles are calculated in the same way. Results are summarized in Table 7-1 and the circles drawn in Fig. 7-2.

TABLE 7-1   VALUES FOR EXAMPLE 7-1

G_1 dB	-1	0	1	2	3
G_1 ratio	0.79	1	1.26	1.59	2
g_1	0.29	0.36	0.45	0.57	0.72
d_1	0.43	0.49	0.55	0.63	0.70
ρ_1	0.55	0.49	0.41	0.33	0.23

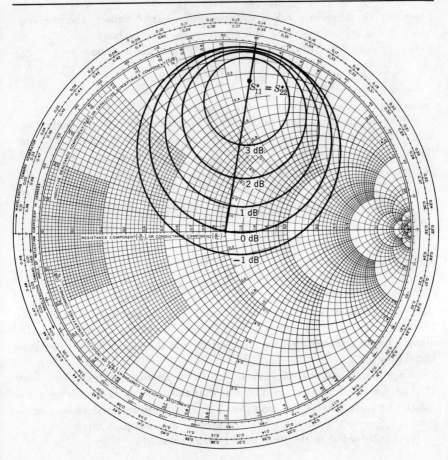

Figure 7-2.   Power-gain circles for Example 7-1.

7-22   Case B: $|S_{ii}| > 1$

Whenever values of $|S_{ii}| > 1$ are encountered, the device is potentially unstable as discussed in Section 6.6, because the point would be located outside the Smith chart where negative input or output resistance is obtained. This normally does not cause difficulty when measuring the S parameters, because of the 50-Ω reference terminations of the measuring system. If the net total input or output loop resistance is positive, the circuit will not oscillate during the S parameter measurements. This constitutes a very powerful aspect of the S parameter approach.

When $|S_{ii}| > 1$, the Smith chart can still be used by locating the reciprocal of the conjugate of the S_{ii} involved, as discussed in Section 3-12. But now the resistance markings are taken to represent negative values, and the reactance markings are the same as marked on the Smith chart.

It is again helpful to define a normalized gain factor to be

$$g_i = G_i(1 - |S_{ii}|^2) \tag{39}$$

Since $|S_{ii}| > 1$, the value of g_i will be negative.

Following the procedures of Section 7-21, the location of the centers and the radii of constant-power-gain circles turn out to be the same as before. Thus

$$d_i = \frac{g_i|S_{ii}|}{1 - |S_{ii}|^2(1 - g_i)} \tag{40}$$

and

$$\rho_i = \frac{\sqrt{1 - g_i}\,(1 - |S_{ii}|^2)}{1 - |S_{ii}|^2(1 - g_i)} \tag{41}$$

The numbers substituted for g_i in (40) and (41) are negative as determined from (39), but d_i and ρ_i are positive. The centers of the circles are located along a line drawn between the chart origin and the point $1/S_{ii}$, as discussed in Section 7-21.

So again a family of circles can be drawn for specified values of the factor G_i. The main difference from case A is that now the resistance circles of the Smith chart are taken to be negative. The amount of negative resistance for constant G_i varies from point to point around a power-gain circle.

The contribution to the total power gain provided by G_i is

$$G_i = \frac{|1 - |r_i|^2|}{|1 - r_i S_{ii}|^2} \tag{42}$$

The maximum value of G_i is infinite for a critical value $r_i = r_{ic} = 1/S_{ii}$. This critical reflection coefficient can be produced by a critical passive terminating impedance Z_{ic} whose positive resistive component equals the magnitude of the negative input or output resistance owing to $|S_{ii}| > 1$. Since the total loop resistance is zero in such a situation, oscillation occurs.

In order to prevent oscillation at the ith port, r_i must be chosen such that the real part of the terminating impedance is larger than the magnitude of the negative resistance corresponding to the point $1/S_{ii}$. This is easily accomplished because that region of the Smith chart where the markings on the resistance circles are less in magnitude than for the one passing through the point $1/S_{ii}$ represents the unstable region.

Example 7-2.

A measurement on a transistor in a 50-Ω system gives

$$S_{11} = 2.5 \underline{/126.9^\circ}$$

(a) Determine the input impedance of the transistor with 50-Ω terminations.
(b) Locate the unstable region on the Smith chart.
(c) Construct a power-gain circle for $G_1 = 6$ dB.
(d) Determine the source impedance Z_1 that will provide the greatest degree of stability against oscillation as well as $G_1 = 6$ dB.

Solution

(a) Locate $1/S_{11}^* = 0.4 \underline{/126.9^\circ}$ as shown in Fig. 7-2. The normalized input impedance at $1/S_{11}^*$ is $Z_{11}/R_0 \cong -0.51 + j0.39$ because the resistance circles are taken to be negative at that point. This can also be calculated from (6-56). Solve for normalized input impedance to obtain

$$\frac{Z_{11}}{R_0} = \frac{1 + S_{11}}{1 - S_{11}} = \frac{1 - 1.5 + j2}{1 + 1.5 - j2} = -0.512 + j0.39$$

which agrees with the Smith-chart value. The input impedance is

$$Z_{11} \cong 50(-0.51 + j0.39) = -25.5 + j19.5 \ \Omega.$$

(b) The unstable region is crosshatched in Fig. 7-3. If reflection coefficient is chosen anywhere in this region, the resistive part for the source impedance Z_1 is equal to or less than the magnitude of $-25.5 \ \Omega$, resulting in a net zero or negative input loop resistance. (c) $G_i = 6$ dB corresponds to a power ratio of 3.98. Then, from (39),

$$g_1 = G_1(1 - |S_{11}|^2) = 3.98(1 - 6.25) = -20.9$$

From (40), the distance from the origin to the center of a $G_1 = 6$ dB circle, along a line through $1/S_{11}$, is

$$d_1 = \frac{g_1|S_{11}|}{1 - |S_{11}|^2(1 - g_1)} = \frac{-20.9(2.5)}{1 - 6.25(1 + 20.9)} = 0.384$$

From (41), the radius of the circle for $G_1 = 6$ dB is

$$\rho_1 = \frac{\sqrt{1 - g_1} \ (1 - |S_{11}|^2)}{1 - |S_{11}|^2(1 - g_1)} = \frac{\sqrt{21.9} \ (-5.25)}{-136} = 0.181$$

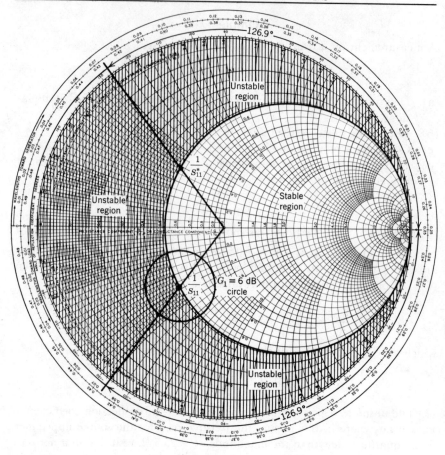

Figure 7-3. Construction for Example 7-2.

The circle is drawn in Fig. 7-3. (*d*) The greatest degree of stability is obtained by choosing r_1 on the $G_1 = 6$ dB circle such that the real part of Z_1 is the most positive. This occurs where a resistance circle for 0.78 is tangent to the $G_1 = 6$ dB circle. Thus $r_1 = 0.78 - j0.38$, or $Z_1 = 50(0.78 - j0.38) = 39 - j19 \, \Omega$. Since the net resistance of the input loop is $39 - 25.5 = +13.5 \, \Omega$, the input port is stable.

7.23 A Broadband Design

The scattering parameters of a transistor vary with frequency. Such variations are not especially significant in narrowband amplifiers. However, in wideband amplifiers, the variations can be so large that they need to be taken into account in order for the transducer power gain to be essentially constant.

As shown in Section 7-2, unilateral transducer power gain is

$$(G'_T)_u = G_T G_1 G_2 \tag{43}$$

where $G_T = |S_{21}|^2$, and G_1 and G_2 represent any additional power gain or loss obtained by matching or mismatching the input and output circuits. Therefore, essentially constant transducer power gain can be obtained at selected frequencies by purposely mismatching the input and output circuits such that the variations of G_1 or G_2 compensate for variations of G_T.

After determining how G_T varies, select values for G_1 or G_2 that make the unilateral power gain essentially constant. Draw the required power-gain circles, and then design the input and output circuits.

The location of the center and the radius of a power-gain circle are repeated here as

$$d_i = \frac{g_i |S_{ii}|}{1 - |S_{ii}|^2 (1 - g_i)} \qquad i = 1, 2 \tag{44}$$

and

$$\rho_i = \frac{\sqrt{1 - g_i} \ (1 - |S_{ii}|^2)}{1 - |S_{ii}|^2 (1 - g_i)} \qquad i = 1, 2 \tag{45}$$

where $g_i = G_i (1 - |S_{ii}|^2)$.

The procedures are demonstrated by the following example.

Example 7-3.

Design a broadband amplifier to provide a unilateral transducer power gain of 12 dB from 150 to 400 MHz. The scattering parameters for a 50-Ω reference are

150 MHz	250 MHz	400 MHz
$S_{11} = 0.31 \ \underline{/-36°}$	$S_{11} = 0.29 \ \underline{/-55°}$	$S_{11} = 0.25 \ \underline{/-76°}$
$S_{12} = 0$	$S_{12} = 0$	$S_{12} = 0$
$|S_{21}| = 5$	$|S_{21}| = 4$	$|S_{21}| = 2.82$
$S_{22} = 0.91 \ \underline{/-6°}$	$S_{22} = 0.86 \ \underline{/-15°}$	$S_{22} = 0.81 \ \underline{/-26°}$

Solution

The following calculations are made:

150 MHz	250 MHz	400 MHz
$\lvert S_{21}\rvert^2 = 25 = 14$ dB	$\lvert S_{21}\rvert^2 = 16 = 12$ dB	$\lvert S_{21}\rvert^2 = 7.94 = 9$ dB
$G_{1,\max} = 1.11 = 0.45$ dB	$G_{1,\max} = 1.09 = 0.38$ dB	$G_{1,\max} = 1.07 = 0.28$ dB
$G_{2,\max} = 5.8 = 7.6$ dB	$G_{2,\max} = 3.84 = 5.8$ dB	$G_{2,\max} = 2.91 = 4.6$ dB
$G_u \cong 22$ dB	$G_u \cong 18$ dB	$G_u \cong 13.9$ dB

Since $G_{1,\max}$ is so small at all three frequencies, little additional power gain can be obtained by matching the transistor to the 50-Ω source. Hence only the load circuit will be used so that G_2 compensates for the variations in $\lvert S_{21}\rvert^2$.

For 12 dB power gain, the output circuit should make $G_2 = -2$ dB at 150 MHz (to decrease $\lvert S_{21}\rvert^2 = 14$ to 12 dB), 0 dB at 250 MHz (for no change in $\lvert S_{21}\rvert^2 = 12$ dB), and $+3$ dB at 400 MHz (to increase $\lvert S_{21}\rvert^2 = 9$ to 12 dB). Power-gain circles for these three frequencies are drawn as shown in Fig. 7-4, using the following values:

150 MHz	250 MHz	400 MHz
$G_2 = -2$ dB $= 0.631$	$G_2 = 0$ dB $= 1$	$G_2 = 3$ dB $= 2$
$g_2 = 0.1085$	$g_2 = 0.2604$	$g_2 = 0.688$
$d_2 = 0.379$	$d_2 = 0.495$	$d_2 = 0.7$
$\rho_2 = 0.62$	$\rho_2 = 0.495$	$\rho_2 = 0.242$

Because there are three gain conditions, there should be three elements in the output network. Assume three inductors arranged as in Fig. 7-5. L_1, L_2, and L_3 must be found such that the resulting terminations for the transistor are on the appropriate circles.

After some trial and error, the following normalized values are found to be satisfactory:

150 MHz	250 MHz	400 MHz
$+jx_1 = j0.5$	$+jx_1 = +j0.83$	$+jx_1 = +j1.33$
$-jb_2 = -j0.53$	$-jb_2 = -j0.32$	$-jb_2 = -j0.2$
$+jx_3 = +j0.58$	$+jx_3 = +j0.97$	$+jx_3 = +j1.55$

They are shown in Fig. 7-4.

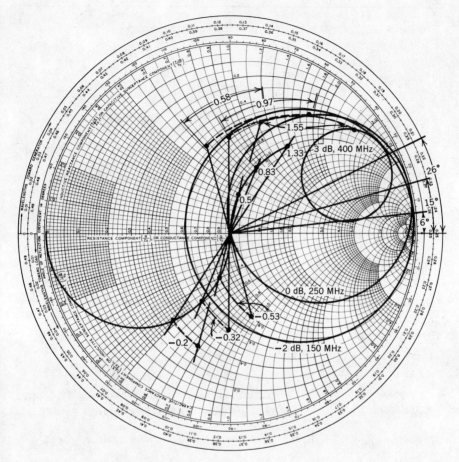

Figure 7-4. Construction for Example 7-3.

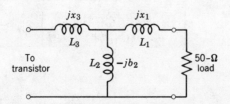

Figure 7-5. Output circuit for Example 7-3.

189

From $x_1 = \omega L_1/50 = 0.5$ at 150 MHz is obtained

$$L_1 = \frac{(0.5)(50)}{2\pi(150)10^6} = 26.5 \text{ nH}$$

From $b_2 = (1/\omega L_2)/(1/50) = 0.53$ at 150 MHz is obtained

$$L_2 = \frac{50}{2\pi(0.53)(150)10^6} = 100 \text{ nH}$$

From $x_3 = \omega L_3/50 = 0.58$ at 150 MHz is obtained

$$L_3 = \frac{(0.58)(50)}{2\pi(150)10^6} = 30.8 \text{ nH}$$

7-24 Unilateral Figure of Merit

The unilateral figure of merit U is useful in determining whether or not, from the standpoint of transducer power gain, the transistor can be considered unilateral.

From (8), the true transducer power gain is

$$|S'_{21}|^2_{\text{true}} = \left|\frac{A_1^*}{A_2}\right|^2 \frac{|S_{21}|^2(1-|r_2|^2)^2}{|(1-r_1 S_{11})(1-r_2 S_{22}) - r_1 r_2 S_{12} S_{21}|^2} \qquad (46)$$

If S_{12} is negligibly small, the unilateral transducer power gain is

$$|S'_{21}|^2_u = \left|\frac{A_1^*}{A_2}\right|^2 \frac{|S_{21}|^2(1-|r_2|^2)^2}{|(1-r_1 S_{11})(1-r_2 S_{22})|^2} \qquad (47)$$

Combine (46) and (47) as

$$|S'_{21}|^2_{\text{true}} = \frac{|S'_{21}|^2_u}{\left|1 - \dfrac{r_1 r_2 S_{12} S_{21}}{(1-r_1 S_{11})(1-r_2 S_{22})}\right|^2} = \frac{|S'_{21}|^2_u}{|1-X|^2} \qquad (48)$$

where

$$X = \frac{r_1 r_2 S_{12} S_{21}}{(1-r_1 S_{11})(1-r_2 S_{22})}. \qquad (49)$$

The ratio of true to unilateral transducer power gains is bounded by

$$\frac{1}{(1+|X|)^2} < \frac{|S'_{21}|^2_{\text{true}}}{|S'_{21}|^2_u} < \frac{1}{(1-|X|)^2} \tag{50}$$

If now $r_1 = S^*_{11}$ and $r_2 = S^*_{22}$, with $|S_{11}| < 1$ and $|S_{22}| < 1$, (50) becomes

$$\frac{1}{(1+U)^2} < \frac{|S'_{21}|^2_{\text{true}}}{|S'_{21}|^2_u} < \frac{1}{(1-U)^2} \tag{51}$$

where

$$U = \frac{|S_{11}||S_{22}||S_{12}||S_{21}|}{(1-|S_{11}|^2)(1-|S_{22}|^2)} \tag{52}$$

The value of U varies with frequency because of the variations of the scattering parameters. At some frequency in the range of interest, U has a maximum. Suppose for example, this maximum is 0.3. Then,

$$\frac{1}{(1+U)^2} = \frac{1}{(1.3)^2} = 0.59 = -2.28 \text{ dB}$$

$$\frac{1}{(1-U)^2} = \frac{1}{(0.7)^2} = 2.04 = 3.1 \text{ dB}$$

Therefore, the ratio of true transducer gain to that obtained by neglecting S_{12} is within a large spread of about 5.4 dB.

If U has a maximum value of 0.03, then,

$$\frac{1}{(1+U)^2} = \frac{1}{(1.03)^2} = 0.943 = -0.26 \text{ dB}$$

$$\frac{1}{(1-U)^2} = \frac{1}{(0.97)^2} = 1.063 = 0.26 \text{ dB}$$

This represents a spread of ± 0.26 dB, so from the standpoint of transducer power gain, S_{12} is sufficiently small to neglect. However, the stability question should be answered as discussed in Section 7-31.

7-3 THE NONUNILATERAL AMPLIFIER

One of the first things to be determined is whether or not the transistor is inherently stable or potentially unstable. This applies even if S_{12} is sufficiently small from the standpoint of transducer power gain to consider the transistor as unilateral.

Stability could be determined by transforming the scattering parameters into the corresponding z, y, or h parameters, and then applying the stability criteria established in Chapter 2. Of course, the entire analysis and design of the amplifier could then follow the procedures previously developed.

However, it is desirable to determine stability criteria directly in terms of measured scattering parameters, as well as the conditions for conjugate matching, the power gains and terminations required, and other nonunilateral properties. It has already been pointed out that, for inherent stability, neither $|S_{11}|$ nor $|S_{22}|$ should be greater than unity.

7-31 Conditions for Inherent Stability

A device is inherently stable if its input and output resistances are positive for any passive terminations. If the input or output resistance is negative, then $|S'_{11}| > 1$ or $|S'_{22}| > 1$ for passive terminations.

Whether or not the input resistance is negative does not depend on the passive source impedance (or its equivalent reflection coefficient r_1). Thus it simplifies analysis to assume $r_1 = 0$ when examining the influence of r_2 on $|S'_{11}|$.

Therefore, for inherent stability, $|S'_{11}| < 1$ for arbitrary passive load terminations (i.e., all r_2 for $|r_2| < 1$), and $|S'_{22}| < 1$ for arbitrary passive source terminations (i.e., all r_1 for $|r_1| < 1$).

Equation 6, with $r_1 = 0$ becomes

$$|S'_{11}| = \frac{|(1 - r_2 S_{22})S_{11} + r_2 S_{12}S_{21}|}{|1 - r_2 S_{22}|} = \frac{|S_{11} - r_2 D_s|}{|1 - r_2 S_{22}|} \tag{53}$$

Equation 9, with $r_2 = 0$ becomes

$$|S'_{22}| = \frac{|(1 - r_1 S_{11})S_{22} + r_1 S_{12}S_{21}|}{|1 - r_1 S_{11}|} = \frac{|S_{22} - r_1 D_s|}{|1 - r_1 S_{11}|} \tag{54}$$

where $D_s = S_{11}S_{22} - S_{12}S_{21}$.

Since (53) and (54) have the same form, any result obtained from one of them yields the result obtained from the other simply by interchanging subscripts ones and twos.

For inherent stability, from (53),

$$|1 - r_2 S_{22}|^2 > |S_{11} - r_2 D_s|^2 \tag{55}$$

where squared magnitudes are used because both sides involve complex quantities. Let $S_{11} = S_{11R} + jS_{11I}$, $S_{22} = S_{22R} + jS_{22I}$, $D_s = D_R + jD_I$, and $r_2 = U_2 + jV_2$, the Smith chart axes. After straightforward but tedious manipulations, a solution of (55) that separates stable and unstable regions is

$$(U_2 - U_{2s})^2 + (V_2 - V_{2s})^2 = \rho_{2s}^2 \tag{56}$$

This represents a family of circles on the Smith chart. The centers are at

$$U_{2s} = \frac{S_{22R} - D_R S_{11R} - D_I S_{11I}}{|S_{22}|^2 - |D_s|^2} = \frac{\text{Re}(S_{22} - D_s S_{11}^*)^*}{|S_{22}|^2 - |D_s|^2} \tag{57}$$

$$V_{2s} = \frac{-S_{22I} - D_R S_{11I} + D_I S_{11R}}{|S_{22}|^2 - |D_s|^2} = \frac{\text{Im}(S_{22} - D_s S_{11}^*)^*}{|S_{22}|^2 - |D_s|^2} \tag{58}$$

which combine to give

$$r_{2s} = U_{2s} + jV_{2s} = \frac{(S_{22} - D_s S_{11}^*)^*}{|S_{22}|^2 - |D_s|^2} \tag{59}$$

as the centers' reflection coefficients.

The radii are given by

$$\rho_{2s} = \frac{|S_{12}S_{21}|}{||S_{22}|^2 - |D_s|^2|} \tag{60}$$

A stability circle is illustrated in Fig. 7-6. The inside of the circle represents the unstable region if some point outside the circle, say at $r_2 = 0$, makes $|S_{11}'| < 1$.

In order for the stable region to extend throughout the entire Smith chart, that is, in order for the device to be inherently stable for all passive loads, it is required that

$$||r_{2s}| - \rho_{2s}| > 1 \tag{61}$$

Then the unstable region lies beyond the Smith chart border.

Using (57), (58), (59), and (60), this condition for inherent stability becomes

$$\left| \frac{|S_{22} - D_s S_{11}^*| - |S_{12}S_{21}|}{|S_{22}|^2 - |D_s|^2} \right| > 1 \tag{62}$$

Interchanging subscripts ones and twos gives the corresponding condition for

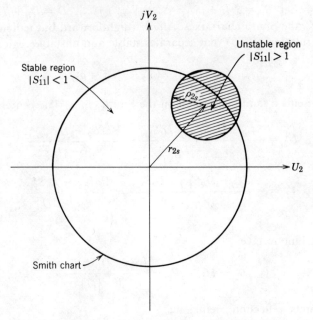

Figure 7-6. Possible stable and unstable regions on the Smith chart.

the input circuit

$$\left| \frac{|S_{11} - D_s S_{22}^*| - |S_{12}S_{21}|}{|S_{11}|^2 - |D_s|^2} \right| > 1 \tag{63}$$

Condition 62 can be rearranged as follows:

$$\left| |S_{22} - D_s S_{11}^*| - |S_{12}S_{21}| \right|^2 > \left| |S_{22}|^2 - |D_s|^2 \right|^2 \tag{64}$$

Square and group terms:

$$2|S_{12}S_{21}||S_{22} - D_s S_{11}^*| < |S_{22} - D_s S_{11}^*|^2 + |S_{12}S_{21}|^2 - \left| |S_{22}|^2 - |D_s|^2 \right|^2$$

Square again, substitute the identity

$$|S_{22} - D_s S_{11}^*|^2 = |S_{12}S_{21}|^2 + (1 - |S_{11}|^2)(|S_{22}|^2 - |D_s|^2)$$

Cancel and combine terms to obtain

$$(|S_{22}|^2 - |D_s|^2)^2 \left\{ \left[(1 - |S_{11}|^2) - (|S_{22}|^2 - |D_s|^2) \right]^2 - 4|S_{12}S_{21}|^2 \right\} > 0$$

which results in

$$2|S_{12}S_{21}| < 1 - |S_{11}|^2 - |S_{22}|^2 + |D_s|^2 \tag{65}$$

The same procedure starting with (63), gives the same result as (65). Therefore the two conditions (62) and (63) have been combined into a single one in (65).

Other results can be obtained from (65). Expand (65), multiply by $(1 - |S_{11}|^2)$, and rearrange terms to obtain

$$(1 - |S_{11}|^2)|S_{22}|^2 + |S_{11}|^2|S_{12}S_{21}|^2 + 2(1 - |S_{11}|^2)\operatorname{Re}(S_{12}^*S_{21}^*S_{11}S_{22})$$

$$< (1 - |S_{11}|^2)^2 - 2|S_{12}S_{21}|(1 - |S_{11}|^2) + |S_{12}S_{21}|^2 \tag{66}$$

This can be expressed as

$$\left[S_{22R}(1 - |S_{11}|^2) + S_{11R}\operatorname{Re}(S_{12}S_{21}) + S_{11I}\operatorname{Im}(S_{12}S_{21}) \right]^2$$

$$+ \left[S_{22I}(1 - |S_{11}|^2) + S_{11R}\operatorname{Im}(S_{12}S_{21}) - S_{11I}\operatorname{Re}(S_{12}S_{21}) \right]^2$$

$$< (1 - |S_{11}|^2 - |S_{12}S_{21}|)^2 \tag{67}$$

This is the same as

$$\left| S_{22} + \frac{S_{11}^*S_{12}S_{21}}{1 - |S_{11}|^2} \right|^2 < \left(1 - \frac{|S_{12}S_{21}|}{1 - |S_{11}|^2} \right)^2 \tag{68}$$

Taking the square root, we get

$$\left| S_{22} + \frac{S_{11}^*S_{12}S_{21}}{1 - |S_{11}|^2} \right| < 1 - \frac{|S_{12}S_{21}|}{1 - |S_{11}|^2} \tag{69}$$

This is true only if the right-hand side is positive. Thus,

$$|S_{12}S_{21}| < 1 - |S_{11}|^2 \tag{70}$$

Interchanging subscripts in (70) yields

$$|S_{12}S_{21}| < 1 - |S_{22}|^2 \tag{71}$$

Conditions (65), (70), and (71) are relatively simple to work with.

If (71) is true, the quantity $B_1 = 1 + |S_{11}|^2 - |S_{22}|^2 - |D_s|^2$ is positive. This is shown in Appendix B.

If (70) is true, the quantity $B_2 = 1 + |S_{22}|^2 - |S_{11}|^2 - |D_s|^2$ is positive as shown in Appendix B.

In summary, the conditions for inherent stability are

$$|S_{12}S_{21}| < 1 - |S_{11}|^2 \tag{72}$$

$$|S_{12}S_{21}| < 1 - |S_{22}|^2 \tag{73}$$

$$2|S_{12}S_{21}| < 1 - |S_{11}|^2 - |S_{22}|^2 + |D_s|^2 \tag{74}$$

Condition 74 may be expressed as

$$K > 1 \tag{75}$$

where

$$K = \frac{1 - |S_{11}|^2 - |S_{22}|^2 + |D_s|^2}{2|S_{12}S_{21}|} \tag{76}$$

Of course, (72) and (73) are meaningful only if $|S_{11}| < 1$ and $|S_{22}| < 1$. As indicated above, (72) and (73) imply that $B_1 > 0$ and $B_2 > 0$. However, even if (72) or (73) does not hold, B_1 or B_2 may still be positive. (See Problem 7-6c.)

Example 7-4

Determine stability for each of the following:

(a) $S_{11} = 0.277 \underline{/-59°}$ (b) $S_{11} = 0.43 \underline{/-55°}$ (c) $S_{11} = 0.43 \underline{/-55°}$

$S_{12} = 0.078 \underline{/93°}$ $S_{12} = 0.091 \underline{/76°}$ $S_{12} = 0.091 \underline{/76°}$

$S_{21} = 1.92 \underline{/64°}$ $S_{21} = 3.4 \underline{/62°}$ $S_{21} = 2.4 \underline{/62°}$

$S_{22} = 0.848 \underline{/-31°}$ $S_{22} = 0.91 \underline{/-43°}$ $S_{22} = 0.91 \underline{/-43°}$

Solution

(a) For inherent stability:

$$|S_{12}S_{21}| < 1 - |S_{11}|^2 \quad \text{or} \quad 0.1498 < 1 - 0.0767 = 0.9233$$

$$|S_{12}S_{21}| < 1 - |S_{22}|^2 \quad \text{or} \quad 0.1498 < 1 - 0.7191 = 0.2809$$

$$K = \frac{1 + |D_s|^2 - |S_{11}|^2 - |S_{22}|^2}{2|S_{12}S_{21}|} = 1.032 > 1$$

The transistor is inherently stable. Also,

$$B_1 = 1 + |S_{11}|^2 - |S_{22}|^2 - |D_s|^2 = 0.253 > 0$$

and

$$B_2 = 1 + |S_{22}|^2 - |S_{11}|^2 - |D_s|^2 = 1.54 > 0$$

(b)

$$|S_{12}S_{21}| < 1 - |S_{11}|^2 \qquad \text{or} \qquad 0.3094 < 1 - 0.1849 = 0.8151$$

$$|S_{12}S_{21}| < 1 - |S_{22}|^2 \qquad \text{or} \qquad 0.3094 < 1 - 0.8281 = 0.1719$$

So the transistor is potentially unstable. Also,

$$B_1 = 1 + |S_{11}|^2 - |S_{22}|^2 - |D_s|^2 = -0.0274 < 0$$

(c)

$$|S_{12}S_{21}| < 1 - |S_{11}|^2 \qquad \text{or} \qquad 0.2184 < 1 - 0.1849 = 0.8151$$

$$|S_{12}S_{21}| < 1 - |S_{22}|^2 \qquad \text{or} \qquad 0.2184 < 1 - 0.8281 = 0.1719$$

So the transistor is potentially unstable. Also, $B_1 = 0.0605 > 0$. It turns out that $B_1 > 0$ even though the transistor is potentially unstable. Using $B_1 > 0$ as a condition for inherent stability is not valid.

7-32 Power–Gain Circles

Since operating power gain is independent of source impedance, it is convenient to let $r_1 = 0$ when using (10). The operating power gain is

$$G_p' = \frac{|S_{21}'|^2}{1 - |S_{11}'|^2} = \frac{|S_{21}|^2 |1 - |r_2|^2|}{|1 - r_2 S_{22}|^2 - |S_{11} - r_2 D_s|^2} \tag{77}$$

This can be expressed as

$$G_p' = |S_{21}|^2 g_2 \tag{78}$$

where

$$g_2 = \frac{|1 - |r_2|^2|}{|1 - |S_{11}|^2 + |r_2|^2(|S_{22}|^2 - |D_s|^2) - 2\operatorname{Re}(r_2 C_2)|} \tag{79}$$

and

$$C_2 = S_{22} - D_s S_{11}^* \tag{80}$$

For a constant operating power gain,

$$g_2 = \frac{G_p'}{|S_{21}|^2} \tag{81}$$

Letting $r_2 = U_2 + jV_2$, and using $\mathrm{Re}(r_2 C_2) = U_2 \mathrm{Re}\, C_2 - V_2 \mathrm{Im}\, C_2$, (79) becomes

$$(U_2 - U_{2c})^2 + (V_2 - V_{2c})^2 = \rho_{2c}^2 \tag{82}$$

$$U_{2c} = \frac{g_2 \mathrm{Re}\, C_2^*}{1 + g_2(|S_{22}|^2 - |D_s|^2)} \tag{83}$$

$$V_{2c} = \frac{g_2 \mathrm{Im}\, C_2^*}{1 + g_2(|S_{22}|^2 - |D_s|^2)} \tag{84}$$

$$\rho_{2c} = \frac{\sqrt{1 - 2K|S_{12}S_{21}|\, g_2 + |S_{12}S_{21}|^2 g_2^2}}{1 + g_2(|S_{22}|^2 - |D_s|^2)} \tag{85}$$

and

$$K = \frac{1 - |S_{11}|^2 - |S_{22}|^2 + |D_s|^2}{2|S_{12}S_{21}|} \tag{86}$$

The centers of the power-gain circles are located along a line at an angle

$$\phi = \tan^{-1} \frac{\mathrm{Im}\, C_2^*}{\mathrm{Re}\, C_2^*} \tag{87}$$

The radius given by (85) was obtained after using the identity

$$|S_{22} - D_s S_{11}^*|^2 = |S_{12}S_{21}|^2 + (1 - |S_{11}|^2)(|S_{22}|^2 - |D_s|^2)$$

The centers are located at

$$r_{2c} = U_{2c} + jV_{2c} = \frac{g_2 C_2^*}{1 + g_2(|S_{22}|^2 - |D_s|^2)} \tag{88}$$

Instability is indicated by infinite operating power gain, or by $g_2 = \infty$. Thus letting g_2 approach infinity in (85) and (88) leads to the radius ρ_{2s} and the center location r_{2s} of the stability circle found in Section 7-31.

Maximum operating power gain occurs at the point in the r_2 plane for which the radius $\rho_{2c} = 0$. Thus, from (85),

$$g_{20}^2 - \frac{2K}{|S_{12}S_{21}|} g_{20} + 1 = 0 \tag{89}$$

so that

$$g_{20} = \frac{1}{|S_{12}S_{21}|} \left(K \pm \sqrt{K^2 - 1} \right) \tag{90}$$

Then, substituting (90) into (78), the maximum operating power gain is

$$G'_{p,\max} = \frac{|S_{21}|}{|S_{12}|} \left(K \pm \sqrt{K^2 - 1} \right) \tag{91}$$

In (90) and (91), the minus sign is used with inherent stability.

For each value of r_2 used for the power gain desired, maximum output power occurs with a conjugate match at the input for which $S'_{11} = 0$. Thus

$$(1 - r_2 S_{22})(S_{11} - r_1^*) + r_2 S_{12} S_{21} = 0 \tag{92}$$

From which the required value of r_1 is found to be

$$r_1 = \left(\frac{S_{11} - r_2 D_s}{1 - r_2 S_{22}} \right)^* \tag{93}$$

Example 7-5.

Draw several power-gain circles for the transistor of Example 7-4a.

Solution

The transistor has been shown to be inherently stable with $K = 1.032$ and $B_1 > 0$. The maximum operating power gain is

$$G'_{p,\max} = \frac{|S_{21}|}{|S_{12}|} \left(K - \sqrt{K^2 - 1} \right)$$

$$= \frac{1.920}{0.078} \left(1.032 - \sqrt{(1.032)^2 - 1} \right) = 19.1 = 12.8 \, \text{dB}$$

also,

$$g_{20} = \frac{1}{|S_{12}S_{21}|} \left(K - \sqrt{K^2 - 1} \right) = 5.19$$

or

$$g_{20} = \frac{G'_{p,\max}}{|S_{12}|^2} = \frac{19.13}{(1.92)^2} = 5.19$$

and

$$C_2^* = S_{22}^* - D_s^* S_{11} = 0.7678 \underline{/33.85°}$$

The centers of the circles lie on a line through the origin at the angle $33.85°$. The maximum-power-gain point is located at

$$r_{20} = \frac{g_{20} C_2^*}{1 + g_{20}(|S_{22}|^2 - |D_s|^2)} = 0.952 \underline{/33.85°}$$

In making calculations for a circle, assume a power gain G'_p, calculate $g_2 = G'_p/|S_{21}|^2$, then the radius and location of the center. It is helpful to calculate separately the various quantities involving scattering parameters for use whenever needed.

Results of the calculations are given in Table 7-2. Circles are drawn in Fig. 7-7.

TABLE 7-2 LOCATIONS AND RADII FOR POWER-GAIN CIRCLES

G'_p		g_2	ρ_2	$|r_2|$
dB	Ratio			
12.8	19.1	5.19	0	0.952
11.8	15.1	4.10	0.094	0.895
9.8	9.6	2.59	0.228	0.768
7.8	6	1.63	0.370	0.630
5.8	3.8	1.03	0.515	0.485
2.8	1.9	0.518	0.700	0.300

The normalized load impedance for $r_{20} = 0.952 \underline{/33.85°}$ is $Z_L/50 = 0.29 + j3.26$, so $Z_L = 14.5 + j163$ Ω. The input reflection coefficient for a conjugate match is

$$r_1 = \left(\frac{S_{11} - r_{20} D_s}{1 - r_{20} S_{22}} \right)^* = 0.733 \underline{/135.5°}$$

Therefore the normalized source impedance is $Z_s/50 = 0.18 + j0.4$, so $Z_s = 9 + j20$ Ω.

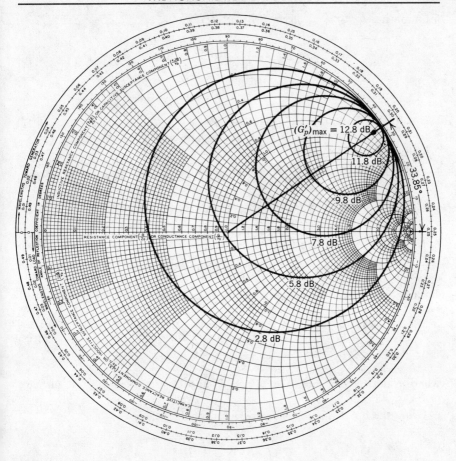

Figure 7-7. Power-gain circles for Example 7-5.

7-33 Simultaneous Conjugate Matching

If a two-port network is conjugate matched at both ports simultaneously, then $S'_{11}=0$ and $S'_{22}=0$. The optimum terminations for these matched conditions require reflection coefficients r_{1m} and r_{2m}.

To make $S'_{11}=0$ and $S'_{22}=0$ with $r_1=r_{1m}$ and $r_2=r_{2m}$, the numerators of (6) and (9) must equal zero. Thus,

$$(1-r_{2m}S_{22})(S_{11}-r^*_{1m})+r_{2m}S_{12}S_{21}=0 \tag{94}$$

and

$$(1-r_{1m}S_{22})(S_{22}-r^*_{2m})+r_{1m}S_{12}S_{21}=0 \tag{95}$$

Eliminating r_{1m} and r_{2m} from (94) and (95) yields

$$r_{2m}^2 - r_{2m}\frac{B_2}{C_2} + \frac{C_2^*}{C_2} = 0 \tag{96}$$

and

$$r_{1m}^2 - r_{1m}\frac{B_1}{C_1} + \frac{C_1^*}{C_1} = 0 \tag{97}$$

where

$$B_1 = 1 + |S_{11}|^2 - |S_{22}|^2 - |D_s|^2 = \text{a real number} \tag{98}$$

$$B_2 = 1 + |S_{22}|^2 - |S_{11}|^2 - |D_s|^2 = \text{a real number} \tag{99}$$

$$C_1 = S_{11} - S_{22}^* D_s = \text{a complex number} \tag{100}$$

$$C_2 = S_{22} - S_{11}^* D_s = \text{a complex number} \tag{101}$$

Because of the similarity of (96) and (97), consider

$$r_{im}^2 - r_{im}\frac{B_i}{C_i} + \frac{C_i^*}{C_i} = 0 \tag{102}$$

where i can have values 1 or 2, and B_i and C_i are given by (98) through (101).

Using the quadratic formula, the solution of (102) is

$$r_{im} = \frac{C_i^*}{|C_i|}\left(\frac{B_i}{2|C_i|} \pm \sqrt{\left|\frac{B_i}{2C_i}\right|^2 - 1}\right) \tag{103}$$

Examination of (103) shows that if $|B_i/2C_i| < 1$, then $|r_{im}| = 1$, so that the source and load resistances are zero. If $|B_i/2C_i| > 1$, one of the two solutions for r_{im} has a magnitude greater than unity (i.e., that termination is not passive), and the other solution has a magnitude less than unity. The solution less than unity is the useful one, and is obtained from (103) using the minus sign if B_i is positive. If B_i is negative, the device is potentially unstable.

Example 7-6

Determine the optimum terminations for simultaneous conjugate matching using the transistor of Example 7-4a.

Solution

The transistor is inherently stable with $K = 1.032$, $B_1 = 0.2525$, $B_2 = 1.537$, $C_1 = 0.1203 \underline{/-135.4°}$, and $C_2 = 0.768 \underline{/-33.85°}$. Then

$$r_{1m} = \frac{C_1^*}{|C_1|}\left(\frac{B_1}{2|C_1|} - \sqrt{\left|\frac{B_1}{2C_1}\right|^2 - 1} \right)$$

$$= 0.731 \underline{/+135.4°}$$

and

$$r_{2m} = \frac{C_2^*}{|C_2|}\left(\frac{B_2}{2|C_2|} - \sqrt{\left|\frac{B_2}{2C_2}\right|^2 - 1} \right)$$

$$= 0.958 \underline{/33.85°}$$

both of which agree closely with the results of Example 7-5. Therefore Z_L, Z_s, and the power gain are the same as in Example 7-5.

7-34 Design Using Potentially Unstable Transistors

Design procedures are move involved when the transistor is potentially unstable. The output circuit stability circle (or portion thereof) is drawn on a Smith chart. After a power gain is selected, a power-gain circle is drawn. Choose a value of r_2 at a point on the power-gain circle that is not in the unstable region but well within the stable region. Knowing r_2, the Smith chart coordinates give the normalized load impedance.

Then the source reflection coefficient is chosen. If a conjugate matched input circuit is acceptable, calculate

$$r_1 = \left(\frac{S_{11} - r_2 D_s}{1 - r_2 S_{22}} \right)^* \tag{104}$$

To determine if this r_1 is acceptable, draw an input circuit stability circle (or portion thereof) and locate r_1. This r_1 is acceptable provided it is not in the input circuit unstable region nor too close to the input circuit stability circle. A reflection coefficient too close to a stability circle may move into the unstable region when tuning adjustments are made.

Example 7-7 illustrates the procedures.

Example 7-7

The scattering parameters of a transistor in a 50-Ω system are

$$S_{11} = 0.43 \, \underline{/-55°} \qquad S_{12} = 0.091 \, \underline{/76°}$$

$$S_{21} = 2.4 \, \underline{/62°} \qquad S_{22} = 0.91 \, \underline{/-43°}$$

Select terminating impedances for an operating power gain of 8 dB.

Solution

The power gain is

$$G'_p = 10^{0.8} = 6.31$$

Several calculations are needed.

$$|S_{12}S_{21}| = 0.218 \qquad |S_{11}|^2 = 0.185 \qquad |S_{22}|^2 = 0.828$$

$$D_s = S_{11}S_{22} - S_{12}S_{21} = 0.544 \, \underline{/-78.6°}$$

$$|D_s|^2 = 0.296 \qquad g_2 = G'_p / |S_{21}|^2 = 1.1$$

$$K = \frac{1 - |S_{11}|^2 - |S_{22}|^2 + |D_s|^2}{2|S_{12}S_{21}|} = 0.649$$

The transistor is potentially unstable because $K < 1$.

$$B_1 = 1 + |S_{11}|^2 - |S_{22}|^2 - |D_s|^2 = 0.0604$$

$$B_2 = 1 + |S_{22}|^2 - |S_{11}|^2 - |D_s|^2 = 1.347$$

$$C_1 = S_{11} - S_{22}^* D_s = 0.169 \, \underline{/-157.7°}$$

$$C_2 = S_{22} - S_{11}^* D_s = 0.694 \, \underline{/-49.5°}$$

The center of the output circuit stability circle is

$$r_{2s} = \frac{C_2^*}{|S_{22}|^2 - |D_s|^2} = 1.305 \, \underline{/49.5°}$$

The radius of the output circuit stability circle is

$$\rho_{2s} = \frac{|S_{12}S_{21}|}{||S_{22}|^2 - |D_s|^2|} = 0.411$$

The center of the power-gain circle is

$$r_{2c} = \frac{g_2 C_2^*}{1 + g_2(|S_{22}|^2 - |D_s|^2)} = 0.481 \underline{/49.5°}$$

The radius of the power-gain circle is

$$\rho_{2c} = \frac{\sqrt{1 - 2K|S_{12}S_{21}|g_2 + |S_{12}S_{21}|^2 g_2^2}}{1 + g_2(|S_{22}|^2 - |D_s|^2)} = 0.545$$

These circles are drawn in Figure 7-8 and r_2 selected. If $r_2 = 0.081 \underline{/-84.5°}$, then $Z_L/50 = 1 - j0.16$, or $Z_L = 50 - j8 \ \Omega$.

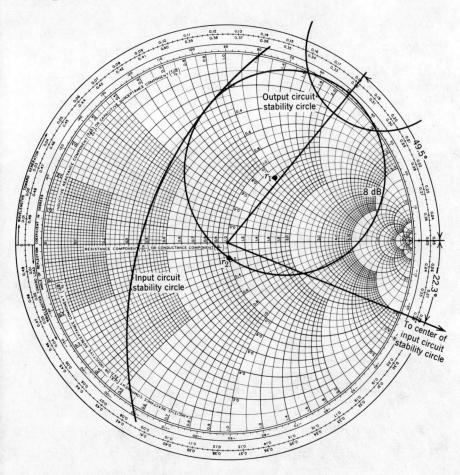

Figure 7-8. Constructions for Example 7-7.

For a conjugate matched input circuit,

$$r_1 = \left(\frac{S_{11} - r_2 D_s}{1 - r_2 S_{22}} \right)^* = 0.426 \,\underline{/52.8^\circ}$$

To determine if this r_1 is acceptable, draw the input circuit stability circle whose center is

$$r_{1s} = \frac{C_1^*}{|S_{11}|^2 - |D_s|^2} = 1.51 \,\underline{/-22.3^\circ}$$

and whose radius is

$$\rho_{1s} = \frac{|S_{12} S_{21}|}{||S_{11}|^2 - |D_s|^2|} = 1.96$$

and then locate r_1 as shown in Figure 7-8. It is seen that this r_1 is an acceptable reflection coefficient because it is inside the input circuit stable region. It may not always be possible to select r_2 anywhere on the chosen power gain circle such that r_1 is in the stable region. If not, either r_1 can be selected arbitrarily to be in the stable region (but then the input circuit is not conjugate matched), or the power gain must be changed.

PROBLEMS

7-1. Design matching networks for the amplifier of Example 7-1 to provide maximum power gain using
(a) ell sections
(b) microstrip lines and stubs.

7-2. The scattering parameters of a transistor in a 50-Ω system are

$$S_{11} = 0.455 \,\underline{/-63.4^\circ} \qquad S_{12} = 0$$

$$|S_{21}| = 5 \qquad S_{22} = 0.707 \,\underline{/-10.5^\circ}$$

Determine:
(a) maximum power gain
(b) optimum terminations
(c) power-gain circles for G_2 of -1 dB, 0 dB, $+1$ dB, and for G_1 of 0 dB.

7-3. The scattering parameters of a transistor in a 50-Ω system are

$$S_{11} = 2.5 \,\underline{/-45^\circ} \qquad S_{12} = 0$$

$$|S_{21}| = 5 \qquad S_{22} = 0.9 \,\underline{/-20^\circ}$$

(a) Design output matching network for $G_{2,\max}$.

(b) Design input matching network for $G_1 = 6$ dB with the greatest degree of stability.

(c) Determine unilateral transducer power gain.

7-4. Design a broadband amplifier to provide a power gain of 8 dB at 100 MHz, 300 MHz and 500 MHz. The scattering parameters for a 50-Ω system are

	100 MHz	300 MHz	500 MHz
$S_{11} =$	$0.62 \underline{/-44°}$	$0.3 \underline{/-81°}$	$0.24 \underline{/-119°}$
$S_{12} =$	0	0	0
$S_{21} =$	$9 \underline{/130°}$	$4 \underline{/91°}$	$2 \underline{/66°}$
$S_{22} =$	$0.9 \underline{/-6°}$	$0.8 \underline{/-14°}$	$0.7 \underline{/-26°}$

7-5. Determine which of the following can be considered unilateral from the standpoint of transducer power gain:

(a) $S_{11} = 0.39 \underline{/-55°}$ (b) $S_{11} = 0.25 \underline{/170°}$

$S_{12} = 0.04 \underline{/90°}$ $S_{12} = 0.2 \underline{/103°}$

$S_{21} = 3 \underline{/78°}$ $S_{21} = 3.7 \underline{/35°}$

$S_{22} = 0.89 \underline{/-26°}$ $S_{22} = 0.88 \underline{/-53°}$

(c) $S_{11} = 0.11 \underline{/-52°}$ (d) $S_{11} = 0.62 \underline{/-44°}$

$S_{12} = 0.02 \underline{/-60°}$ $S_{12} = 0.012 \underline{/75°}$

$S_{21} = 10.4 \underline{/-54°}$ $S_{21} = 9 \underline{/130°}$

$S_{22} = 0.035 \underline{/-60°}$ $S_{22} = 0.96 \underline{/-6°}$

7-6. Determine whether the transistors whose scattering parameters are given in problem 7-5 are inherently stable or potentially unstable.

7-7. Draw several power-gain circles for the transistors of Problem 7-5a and c.

7-8. Design microstrip matching networks for the amplifier of Example 7-6 to convert 50-Ω source and load impedances into the optimum terminations. Express line lengths in wavelengths.

7-9. The scattering parameters of a transistor in a 50-Ω system are

$$S_{11} = 0.11 \underline{/-52°} \qquad S_{12} = 0.02 \underline{/-60°}$$

$$S_{21} = 10.4 \underline{/-54°} \qquad S_{22} = 0.035 \underline{/-60°}$$

Determine terminating impedances and the operating power gain for simultaneous conjugate matching.

7-10. The scattering parameters of a transistor in a 50-Ω system are

$$S_{11} = 0.62 \underline{/-44°} \qquad S_{12} = 0.012 \underline{/75°}$$

$$S_{21} = 9 \underline{/130°} \qquad S_{22} = 0.96 \underline{/-6°}$$

Select terminating impedances for an operating power gain of 15 dB.

APPENDIX A

GENERALIZED SCATTERING PARAMETERS

The purpose of this appendix is to show a derivation for the generalized scattering parameters in terms of the measured scattering parameters and arbitrary terminations. The result is used in Chapter 7.

A three-step procedure is involved.

Step 1. Express the z parameters in terms of the measured scattering parameters and the reference terminating resistances. The matrix symbols [ ] are omitted from the following expressions for simplification because all quantities are matrices.

The open-circuit impedance-parameter matrix relationship is

$$V = zI \tag{1}$$

The normalized incident and reflected components are related to the measured scattering parameters by the matrix expression

$$b = Sa \tag{2}$$

From (6-48), the normalized incident components are related to terminal voltages and currents by

$$a = F(V + R_o I) \tag{3}$$

209

where F is the diagonal matrix given by

$$
F = \tfrac{1}{2}
\begin{bmatrix}
\dfrac{1}{\sqrt{R_o}} & 0 & \cdots & 0 \\
0 & \dfrac{1}{\sqrt{R_o}} & \cdots & 0 \\
\vdots & \vdots & & \vdots \\
0 & 0 & \cdots & \dfrac{1}{\sqrt{R_o}}
\end{bmatrix}
\tag{4a}
$$

and R_o is the diagonal matrix given by

$$
R_o =
\begin{bmatrix}
R_o & 0 & \cdots & 0 \\
0 & R_o & \cdots & 0 \\
\vdots & \vdots & & \vdots \\
0 & 0 & \cdots & R_o
\end{bmatrix}
$$

From (6-53), the normalized reflected components are related to terminal voltages and currents by

$$
b = F(V - R_o I)
\tag{5}
$$

Substitute (3) and (5) into (2) to obtain

$$
FV - FR_o I = SFV + SFR_o I
\tag{6}
$$

Substitute (1) into (6) to eliminate V to obtain

$$
Fz I - FR_o I = SFz I + SFR_o I
$$

Postmultiply by I^{-1} to eliminate current I and rearrange as

$$
Fz - SFz = SFR_o + FR_o = SR_o F + R_o F
\tag{7}
$$

in which $FR_o = R_o F$ because the order of diagonal matrices in multiplication is arbitrary.

Then (7) factors into

$$
(I - S)Fz = (S + I)R_o F
\tag{8}
$$

where I now represents the unit diagonal matrix, and is not to be confused with current I because current has been eliminated in (7). Premultiply (8) first by $(I-S)^{-1}$, then by F^{-1} to obtain

$$z = F^{-1}(I-S)^{-1}(S+I)R_oF \tag{9}$$

Equation (9) is the first relationship sought. Thus the open-circuit-impedance-parameter matrix can be calculated from the product of several known matrices provided the inverse matrices exist.

Step 2. Express the generalized scattering parameters S' in terms of z parameters and arbitrary terminating impedances Z_i. The terminal voltages and currents are still related by

$$V = zI \tag{10}$$

The normalized incident and reflected components for arbitrary terminating impedances are related to the generalized scattering parameters by

$$b' = S'a' \tag{11}$$

From (6-49),

$$a' = G(V+ZI) \tag{12}$$

where

$$G = \tfrac{1}{2}\begin{bmatrix} \dfrac{1}{\sqrt{\operatorname{Re}Z_1}} & 0 & \cdots & 0 \\[2ex] 0 & \dfrac{1}{\sqrt{\operatorname{Re}Z_2}} & \cdots & 0 \\[2ex] \vdots & \vdots & & \vdots \\[2ex] 0 & 0 & \cdots & \dfrac{1}{\sqrt{\operatorname{Re}Z_n}} \end{bmatrix} \tag{12a}$$

and

$$Z = \begin{bmatrix} Z_1 & 0 & \cdots & 0 \\ 0 & Z_2 & \cdots & 0 \\ \vdots & \vdots & \vdots & \vdots \\ 0 & 0 & \cdots & Z_n \end{bmatrix} \tag{12b}$$

From (6-54),

$$b' = G(V - Z*I) \tag{13}$$

Substitute (12) and (13) into (11) to obtain

$$GV - GZ*I = S'GV + S'GZI$$

Substitute (10) into this to obtain

$$GzI - GZ*I = S'GzI + S'GZI$$

Postmultiply by I^{-1} (which eliminates current I) and factor. Thus

$$G(z - Z*) = S'G(z + Z)$$

Postmultiply by $(z + Z)^{-1}$ to obtain

$$G(z - Z*)(z + Z)^{-1} = S'G$$

Then postmultiply by G^{-1}. Thus

$$S' = G(z - Z*)(z + Z)^{-1}G^{-1} \tag{14}$$

Equation 14 is the second relationship sought. This means that the generalized scattering parameters can be calculated from the product of several known matrices provided the inverse matrices exist.

Step 3. Eliminate the z parameters from (14) by using (9). By direct substitution,

$$S' = G\left[F^{-1}(I - S)^{-1}(S + I)R_oF - Z*\right]\left[F^{-1}(I - S)^{-1}(S + I)R_oF + Z\right]^{-1}G^{-1}$$

where I represents the unit diagonal matrix. Using the matrix relationship

$$A^{-1}G^{-1} = (GA)^{-1}$$

in the above, it becomes

$$S' = G\left[F^{-1}(I - S)^{-1}(S + I)R_oF - Z*\right]\left[GF^{-1}(I - S)^{-1}(S + I)R_oF + GZ\right]^{-1}$$

$$\tag{15}$$

Consider the first two factors in (15),

$$G\left[F^{-1}(I - S)^{-1}(S + I)R_oF - Z*\right]$$

Rewrite this as

$$GF^{-1}(I-S)^{-1}[(S+I)R_oF-(I-S)FZ^*]$$

Since F and Z^* are diagonal matrices, they can be interchanged in position to yield, after factoring,

$$GF^{-1}(I-S)^{-1}[(S+I)R_o-(I-S)Z^*]F$$

Expand and rearrange to obtain

$$GF^{-1}(I-S)^{-1}[S(Z^*+R_o)-(Z^*-R_o)]F$$

which can be written as

$$GF^{-1}(I-S)^{-1}\left[S-(Z^*-R_o)(Z^*+R_o)^{-1}\right]F(Z^*+R_o) \qquad (16)$$

Now define a reflection coefficient matrix

$$r=(Z-R_o)(Z+R_o)^{-1}=(Z+R_o)^{-1}(Z-R_o) \qquad (17)$$

Some other matrix relationships are useful at this point. If $r=AB$, then

$$r^*=(AB)^*=A^*B^*$$

Also,

$$(C+D)^*=C^*+D^*$$

Thus, from (17),

$$r^*=(Z^*-R_o)(Z^*+R_o)^{-1}=(Z^*+R_o)^{-1}(Z^*-R_o) \qquad (17a)$$

Therefore (16) becomes

$$GF^{-1}(I-S)^{-1}(S-r^*)F(Z^*+R_o) \qquad (18)$$

This ends considering the first two factors in (15). Now consider the last factor in (15),

$$\left[GF^{-1}(I-S)^{-1}(S+I)R_oF+GZ\right]^{-1}$$

This can be rewritten as

$$\left\{\left[GF^{-1}(I-S)^{-1}\right]\left[(S+I)R_oF+(I-S)FG^{-1}GZ\right]\right\}^{-1}$$

Note that $G^{-1}G=I$. Then interchange F and Z, since they are diagonal matrices, factor, and expand to obtain

$$\left\{\left[GF^{-1}(I-S)^{-1}\right]\left[SR_o+R_o+Z-SZ\right]F\right\}^{-1}$$

Then, collecting terms,

$$\left\{\left[GF^{-1}(I-S)^{-1}\right]\left[Z+R_o-S(Z-R_o)\right]F\right\}^{-1}$$

which can be written as

$$\left\{\left[GF^{-1}(I-S)^{-1}\right]\left[I-S(Z-R_o)(Z+R_o)^{-1}\right]F(Z+R_o)\right\}^{-1}$$

Then, using (17), this becomes

$$\left\{\left[GF^{-1}(I-S)^{-1}\right]\left[(I-Sr)F(Z+R_o)\right]\right\}^{-1}$$

Now use the matrix relationship $A^{-1}B^{-1}=(BA)^{-1}$ in several steps. Thus

$$\left\{\left[(I-S)FG^{-1}\right]^{-1}\left[F^{-1}(I-Sr)^{-1}\right]^{-1}(Z+R_0)\right\}^{-1}$$

and

$$\left\{\left[F^{-1}(I-Sr)^{-1}(I-S)FG^{-1}\right]^{-1}(Z+R_o)\right\}^{-1}$$

or finally,

$$(Z+R_o)^{-1}F^{-1}(I-Sr)^{-1}(I-S)FG^{-1} \qquad (19)$$

This ends consideration of the last factor in (15).

Next, substitute (18) and (19) into (15) to obtain

$$S'=GF^{-1}(I-S)^{-1}(S-r^*)F(Z^*+R_o)(Z+R_o)^{-1}F^{-1}(I-Sr)^{-1}(I-S)FG^{-1}$$

Since diagonal matrices are interchangeable in position, this becomes, with $FF^{-1} = I$,

$$S' = GF^{-1}(I-S)^{-1}(S-r^*)(Z^*+R_o)(Z+R_o)^{-1}(I-Sr)^{-1}(I-S)FG^{-1}$$

(20)

Now, express $(Z^*+R_o)(Z+R_o)^{-1}$ in terms of the reflection coefficient r of (17). Thus

$$I - r = (Z+R_o)^{-1}(Z+R_o) - (Z+R_o)^{-1}(Z-R_o)$$

$$= (Z+R_o)^{-1}(Z+R_o - Z + R_o)$$

$$= (Z+R_o)^{-1}(2R_o)$$

so that

$$I - r^* = (Z^*+R_o)^{-1}(2R_o)$$

and

$$(I-r^*)^{-1} = \left[(Z^*+R_o)^{-1}(2R_o)\right]^{-1} = (2R_o)^{-1}(Z^*+R_o)$$

Therefore

$$(I-r^*)^{-1}(I-r) = (Z^*+R_o)(Z+R_o)^{-1} \tag{21}$$

Substitute (21) into (20) to obtain

$$S' = GF^{-1}(I-S)^{-1}(S-r^*)(I-r^*)^{-1}(I-r)(I-Sr)^{-1}(I-S)FG^{-1} \tag{22}$$

where I represents the unit diagonal matrix. Two other relationships are useful at this point.

1.

$$(I-S)^{-1}(S-r^*)(I-r^*)^{-1} = (I-r^*)^{-1}(S-r^*)(I-S)^{-1} \tag{23}$$

Proof. In the $(S-r^*)$ factors on both sides, add and subtract the unit diagonal matrix I to obtain

$$(I-S)^{-1}[-(I-S)+(I-r^*)](I-r^*)^{-1}$$

$$= (I-r^*)^{-1}[-(I-S)+(I-r^*)](I-S)^{-1}$$

Expand this to obtain

$$-(I-S)^{-1}(I-S)(I-r^*)^{-1}+(I-S)^{-1}(I-r^*)(I-r^*)^{-1}$$

$$=-(I-r^*)^{-1}(I-S)(I-S)^{-1}+(I-r^*)^{-1}(I-r^*)(I-S)^{-1}$$

This simplifies to

$$-(I-r^*)^{-1}+(I-S)^{-1}=-(I-r^*)^{-1}+(I-S)^{-1} \quad \text{Q.E.D.}$$

2.

$$(I-r)(I-Sr)^{-1}(I-S)=(I-S)(I-rS)^{-1}(I-r) \qquad (24)$$

Proof. Write this as

$$\left[(I-Sr)(I-r)^{-1}\right]^{-1}(I-S)=\left[(I-rS)(I-S)^{-1}\right]^{-1}(I-r)$$

then as

$$\left[(I-S)^{-1}(I-Sr)(I-r)^{-1}\right]^{-1}=\left[(I-r)^{-1}(I-rS)(I-S)^{-1}\right]^{-1}$$

or

$$(I-S)^{-1}(I-Sr)(I-r)^{-1}=(I-r)^{-1}(I-rS)(I-S)^{-1}$$

In the $(I-Sr)$ factors, add and subtract r on the left side and S on the right side. Thus

$$(I-S)^{-1}\left[(I-r)+(I-S)r\right](I-r)^{-1}=(I-r)^{-1}\left[(I-S)+(I-r)S\right](I-S)^{-1}$$

Expand to obtain

$$(I-S)^{-1}(I-r)(I-r)^{-1}+(I-S)^{-1}(I-S)r(I-r)^{-1}$$

$$=(I-r)^{-1}(I-S)(I-S)^{-1}+(I-r)^{-1}(I-r)S(I-S)^{-1}$$

which simplifies to

$$(I-S)^{-1}+r(I-r)^{-1}=(I-r)^{-1}+S(I-S)^{-1}$$

Rearrange this as

$$(I-S)^{-1}-S(I-S)^{-1}=(I-r)^{-1}-r(I-r)^{-1}$$

or, after factoring,

$$(I-S)(I-S)^{-1} = (I-r)(I-r)^{-1}$$

$$I = I \qquad \text{Q.E.D.}$$

Now, returning to the original problem, substitute (23) and (24) into (22). Thus

$$S' = GF^{-1}(I-r^*)^{-1}(S-r^*)(I-rS)^{-1}(I-r)FG^{-1} \qquad (25)$$

Define a diagonal matrix A to be

$$A = G^{-1}F(I-r^*) \qquad (26)$$

so that

$$A^{-1} = (I-r^*)^{-1}(G^{-1}F)^{-1} = (I-r^*)^{-1}F^{-1}G$$

$$= GF^{-1}(I-r^*)^{-1}$$

and also

$$A^* = (G^{-1}F)^*(I-r) = (I-r)FG^{-1}$$

in which the positions of diagonal matrices are interchanged, and $F^* = F$ and $(G^{-1})^* = G^{-1}$ because F and G are composed of real components only.
Therefore (25) becomes

$$S' = A^{-1}(S-r^*)(I-rS)^{-1}A^* \qquad (27)$$

Equation 27 is the desired relationship in its most simplified form. It expresses the generalized scattering parameters directly in terms of the measured scattering parameters, the equal reference resistance terminations, and the arbitrary terminating impedances.

When (26) is expanded in terms of the reference resistance and arbitrary terminating impedances, it is found that the ith diagonal component of diagonal matrix A corresponding to the ith port is

$$A_i = \frac{2\sqrt{R_o}\,\sqrt{\mathrm{Re}\,Z_i}}{Z_i^* + R_o} = (1-r_i^*)\sqrt{\frac{\mathrm{Re}\,Z_i}{R_o}} \qquad (28)$$

where R_o is the reference resistance. When expressed in terms of the reflection coefficient r, (28) becomes, after some manipulation,

$$A_i = (1 - r_i^*) \frac{\sqrt{1 - |r_i|^2}}{|1 - r_i|} \qquad (29)$$

where r_i is found from (17) to be

$$r_i = \frac{Z_i - R_o}{Z_i + R_o} \qquad (30)$$

APPENDIX B

SCATTERING PARAMETER INEQUALITIES

If $|S_{12}S_{21}| < 1 - |S_{22}|^2$, then the quantity $B_1 = 1 + |S_{11}|^2 - |S_{22}|^2 - |D_s|^2$ is positive.

Proof.

$$B_1 = 1 + |S_{11}|^2 - |S_{22}|^2 - |S_{11}S_{22} - S_{12}S_{21}|^2$$

$$> |S_{11}|^2 + (1 - |S_{22}|^2) - |S_{11}S_{22}|^2 - 2|S_{11}S_{22}||S_{12}S_{21}| - |S_{12}S_{21}|^2$$

$$> |S_{11}|^2 + |S_{12}S_{21}| - |S_{11}|^2|S_{22}|^2 - 2|S_{11}||S_{22}||S_{12}S_{21}| - |S_{12}S_{21}|^2$$

$$= |S_{12}S_{21}|[1 - 2|S_{11}||S_{22}| - |S_{12}S_{21}|] + |S_{11}|^2[1 - |S_{22}|^2]$$

$$> |S_{12}S_{21}|[1 - 2|S_{11}||S_{22}| - |S_{12}S_{21}|] + |S_{11}|^2|S_{12}S_{21}|$$

$$= |S_{12}S_{21}|[|S_{11}|^2 - 2|S_{11}||S_{22}| + (1 - |S_{12}S_{21}|)]$$

$$> |S_{12}S_{21}|[|S_{11}|^2 - 2|S_{11}||S_{22}| + |S_{22}|^2]$$

$$= |S_{12}S_{21}|[|S_{11}| - |S_{22}|]^2 \geqslant 0$$

Therefore, $B_1 > 0$.

If $|S_{12}S_{21}| < 1 - |S_{11}|^2$, then the quantity $B_2 = 1 + |S_{22}|^2 - |S_{11}|^2 - |D_s|^2$ is positive.

Proof.

$$B_2 = 1 + |S_{22}|^2 - |S_{11}|^2 - |S_{11}S_{22} - S_{12}S_{21}|^2$$

$$> |S_{22}|^2 + (1 - |S_{11}|^2) - |S_{11}S_{22}|^2 - 2|S_{11}S_{22}||S_{12}S_{21}| - |S_{12}S_{21}|^2$$

$$> |S_{22}|^2 + |S_{12}S_{21}| - |S_{11}|^2|S_{22}|^2 - 2|S_{11}||S_{22}||S_{12}S_{21}| - |S_{12}S_{21}|^2$$

$$= |S_{12}S_{21}|[1 - 2|S_{11}||S_{22}| - |S_{12}S_{21}|] + |S_{22}|^2[1 - |S_{11}|^2]$$

$$> |S_{12}S_{21}|[1 - 2|S_{11}||S_{22}| - |S_{12}S_{21}|] + |S_{22}|^2|S_{12}S_{21}|$$

$$= |S_{12}S_{21}|[[|S_{22}|^2 - 2|S_{11}||S_{22}| + (1 - |S_{12}S_{21}|)]]$$

$$> |S_{12}S_{21}|[[|S_{22}|^2 - 2|S_{11}||S_{22}| + |S_{11}|^2]]$$

$$= |S_{12}S_{21}|[[|S_{22}| - |S_{11}|]]^2 \geqslant 0$$

Therefore, $B_2 > 0$.

BIBLIOGRAPHY

Textbooks containing amplifier design techniques:

J. G. Linvill and J. F. Gibbons: *Transistors and Active Circuits*, McGraw-Hill, New York, 1961.

A. J. Coate and J. B. Oakes: *Linear Vacuum-Tube and Transistor Circuits*, McGraw-Hill, New York, 1961.

M. S. Ghausi: *Principles and Design of Linear Active Circuits*, McGraw-Hill, New York, 1965.

K. Kurokawa: *An Introduction to the Theory of Microwave Circuits*, Academic Press, New York, 1969.

C. L. Alley and K. W. Atwood: *Electronic Engineering*, 3rd edition, Wiley, New York, 1973.

The calculus of deviations:

W. W. Happ: "Dynamic Characteristics of 4-Terminal Networks," *IRE Conv. Rec.*, 1954, Part 2, Circuit Theory.

General characteristics of amplifiers:

J. G. Linvill and L. G. Schimpf: "The Design of Tetrode Transistor Amplifiers," *BSTJ*, Vol. 35, July, 1956.

A. P. Stern: "Stability and Power Gain of Tuned Transistor Amplifiers," *Proc. IRE*, Vol. 45, March, 1957.

G. S. Bahrs: "Stable Amplifiers Employing Unstable Transistors," *IRE Conv. Record*, Part 2, 1957.

J. M. Rollet: "Stability and Power-Gain Invariants of Linear Two-Ports," *IRE Trans. Circuit Theory*, March, 1962.

J. O. Scanlon and J. S. Singleton: "The Gain and Stability of Linear Two-Port Amplifiers," *IRE Trans. Circuit Theory*, No. 3, 1962.

Circuit design:

G. Johnson, P. Norris, and F. Opp: "High-Frequency Amplifier Design Using Admittance Parameters," *Electro-Technol.*, Vol. 74, November-December, 1963.

C. M. Puckette: "High-Frequency Amplifiers," *Electro-Technol.*, Vol. 76, December, 1965.

J. Lauchner and M. Silverstein: "Linvill Technique Speeds High Frequency Amplifier Design," *Eng. Bull.*, Motorola Military Electronics Division, Vol. 13, No. 4, 1965.

M. Khazam: "Wideband Amplifier Design," General Radio Experimenter, Vol. 43, No. 1, 1969.

K. Hirano and S. Kanema: "Immittance Transformation of a Two-Port," *Proc. IEEE*, Vol. 56, January, 1968.

V. F. Perna: "Transistor Bandwidths," *Electron. Des.*, Vol. 26, December 20, 1970.

A collection of RF Application Notes has been published by Motorola Semiconductor Products, Inc., Phoenix, Arizona.

The Smith chart:

P. H. Smith: "Transmission Line Calculator," *Electronics*, Vol. 12, January, 1939.

P. H. Smith: "An Improved Transmission Line Calculator," *Electronics*, Vol. 17, January, 1944.

P. H. Smith: "A New Negative Resistance Smith Chart," *Microwave J.*, Vol. 8, June, 1965.

P. H. Smith: *Electronic Applications of the Smith Chart*, McGraw-Hill, New York, 1969.

Graphical design of matching networks:

P. H. Smith: "L-type Impedance Transforming Circuit," *Electronics*, Vol. 15, March, 1942.

H. F. Mathis: "L-Network Design," *Electronics*, Vol. 30, February, 1957.

H. L. Kaylie and R. J. Bosselaers: "Designing π Networks Graphically," *Electron. Prod.*, Vol. 8, February, March, April, 1965.

R. J. Bosselaers: "Design Charts for Tuned Amplifiers," *Electro-Technol.*, Vol. 77, December, 1966.

E. N. Phillips: "Ell-Network Charts Simplify Impedance Matching," *Microwaves*, Vol. 7, May, 1968.

Scattering parameters:

K. Kurokawa: "Power Waves and the Scattering Matrix," *IEEE Trans. MTT*, March, 1965.

A collection of articles on scattering parameters is contained in Hewlett-Packard Application Note 95 entitled: "S-Parameters—Circuit Analysis and Design."

On Q:

E. I. Green: "The Story of Q," *Amer. Sci.*, Vol. 43, October, 1955.

INDEX